GERMAN TANKS
OF
WORLD WAR II

GERMAN TANKS OF WORLD WAR II

DR S. HART & DR R. HART

British Library Cataloguing in Publication Data:
A catalogue record for this book is available
from the British Library

Copyright © 1998 Brown Packaging Books Ltd

ISBN 1-86227-033-3

First published in the UK in 1998 by
Spellmount Limited
The Old Rectory
Staplehurst
Kent TN12 0AZ

1 3 5 7 9 8 6 4 2

Editorial and design: Brown Packaging Books Ltd
Bradley's Close, 74-77 White Lion Street,
London N1 9PF

Editor: Anne Cree
Design: WDA
Picture Research: Ken Botham

Printed in The Czech Republic
60170

Picture credits
Bundesarchiv: 94, 100, 101, 106, 107, 108-109
Robert Hunt Library: 32, 112, 114-115
TRH Pictures: 2-3, 7, 8, 10, 12, 15, 16, 18, 19, 22-23, 24, 28, 31, 36, 37, 38, 42, 43, 44, 46, 48, 50, 51, 53, 54, 57, 58, 60, 62, 64, 66, 67, 68, 69, 70, 73, 74,
78, 80, 81, 82, 86-87, 87, 92-93, 97, 102, 110, 116, 118, 119, 124-125, 126, 128, 129, 130-131, 132, 135, 137, 138, 139, 142-143, 144, 146, 149, 157
TRH Pictures via Espadon: 40, 59

Artwork credits
Aerospace Publishing: 14, 40, 55, 56, 79, 90, 96, 103, 104-105, 127, 155
John Batchelor: 11, 13, 20-21, 30, 35, 47, 52, 63, 65, 72, 75, 77, 98-99, 120-121, 134, 136, 151, 152, 153, 154
Bob Garwood: 26, 85, 113, 122, 123, 156
Salamander Picture Library: 146
Peter Sarson: 140-141

Previous pages: Panzer IV of the *Leibstandarte* Division in southern Russia, March 1944.

CONTENTS

INTRODUCTION

During World War I Germany lagged far behind the Allies in terms of tank development. The Treaty of Versailles of 1919, which prohibited Germany from building or purchasing tanks, perpetuated this backwardness in armoured warfare. Despite such obstacles, during the 1920s the German Army clandestinely developed a few tank prototypes, which it tested at Kazan in the Soviet Union under the terms of a secret treaty signed in 1926 with the Communist regime. After the National Socialist rise to power in Germany in 1933, Hitler soon cast aside existing treaty prohibitions and began a massive rearmament programme. This included the design and mass production of two light training tanks – the Panzer I and II – which were intended as interim stop-gap vehicles, while purpose-built medium and medium/heavy tank designs, Panzer III and IV, were being developed.

Delays in medium tank procurement, however, ensured that in September 1939 the German military went to war still equipped primarily with light tanks. This armoured force now included the valuable Panzer 35(t) and 38(t) tanks taken into German service after the March 1939 Nazi annexation of Czechoslovakia. Despite the growing obsolescence of these light tanks (which became clear during the Western campaign of May–June 1940 and in North Africa during the spring of 1941), desultory medium

LEFT A Panzer IV on the Eastern Front. In many ways this tank was the most important German armoured fighting vehicle of World War II. The Panzer IV was in service as far back as 1936 and, having been rearmed and remodified, was still in action nine years later.

tank production ensured that many light tanks remained in service during the German invasion of the Soviet Union in the summer of 1941.

In combat, the Germans were constantly coming up against superior Soviet tanks. Such bruising encounters generated significant innovations in German armoured fighting vehicle procurement. Such developments included the rapid introduction of a third generation of medium heavy tanks, namely the Panzer V Panther and the Panzer VI Tiger; the up-gunning and up-armouring of the Panzer III and Panzer IV; the marrying of heavy anti-tank guns to obsolete tank chassis to create a series of improvised tank destroyers (Panzerjäger); and the up-gunning of the Sturmgeschütz artillery assault gun to perform in an anti-tank role. Confronted with ever larger numbers of enemy tanks in the second half of the war, the German armoured fighting vehicle inventory proliferated with a new super-heavy tank (the Panzer VI Model B King Tiger) and a series of purpose-built tank destroyers (Jagdpanzer IV, Jagdpanzer 38(t) Hetzer, Jagdpanther and Jagdtiger), and new anti-aircraft tanks, designated Flakpanzer.

Though the quality of German tanks and derivative armoured fighting vehicles was high, the chief weakness of German wartime tank procurement was an inability to produce armour in sufficient quantity. Though Nazi Germany produced some 24,000 tanks and an additional 20,000 armoured fighting vehicles during the war, these totals were far surpassed by both the United States and the Soviet Union. Thus there was never sufficient German armour to maintain battlefield superiority.

CHAPTER I

PANZER I

Nazi Germany's first mass-produced armoured fighting vehicle, the Panzer I, was a stop-gap training vehicle that possessed very limited tactical value on the battlefield. It was a small two-man tank which was inadequate even by the modest standards of the day, but it still fought in Poland and France, and even during the early part of the Russian campaign.

The German Panzer I (Panzerkampfwagen I or armoured fighting vehicle I) design emerged in 1932 as a stop-gap tank to be used primarily for troop training until the proposed Panzer III medium and Panzer IV medium/heavy tanks entered service in the late 1930s. The German Army required a light tank that could be swiftly developed as well as rapidly and cheaply produced. Consequently, in 1932 the German Army Weapons Department purchased a Carden-Loyd Mark IV tankette from the British firm of Vickers to test the suitability of this chassis for mounting a German 2cm gun in a fully revolving turret. The German Army carried out extensive field trials on this tankette, which revealed that the chassis performed best

when carrying a turret that mounted twin machine guns rather than the larger calibre gun. Therefore, the Weapons Department issued specifications to five German firms to construct a prototype five-tonne (4.9-ton) light training tank with a fully revolving turret mounting twin 7.92mm MG 13 machine guns. In December 1933, the German Army selected the Daimler-Benz turret and superstructure and the Krupp chassis for development. The army then contracted Krupp to manufacture three different prototypes, with the proviso that other factories participate in their production so that a range of firms could gain vital experience in tank construction.

Development History

In February 1934, the Krupp factory delivered its LKA1 tank, the first of the prototype vehicles to be completed. After four months of trials, the Weapons Department concluded that the design was satisfactory and placed an initial order with Krupp for 150 vehicles.

LEFT A Panzer I Model B command tank variant – the Kleiner Panzerbefehlswagen I – heads a parade for Axis dignitaries. In the command vehicle, a fixed superstructure that mounted a single machine gun replaces the turret.

The German Army designated these vehicles with the camouflage name Agricultural Tractor Model IA (or LaS IA) to conceal its tank production programme, which was prohibited by the Treaty of Versailles. The High Command also allocated the vehicle the specific ordnance inventory number Sonderkraftfahrzeug (Sdkfz) 101 – by which the vehicle could be uniquely identified. Further orders soon followed and these increased the total LaS IA production run to 300 vehicles.

The LaS IA (Sdkfz) tank was a 5.4-tonne (5.3-ton) vehicle which was operated by a two-man crew and possessed only light 6–13mm (0.2–0.5in) thick armour that offered protection merely against small-arms fire. The vehicle featured a suspension based on four pairs of road wheels and was powered by a 57bhp Krupp M305 B4-cylinder petrol engine that permitted a maximum road speed of 37kph (23mph). Like all subsequent German tanks, every Panzer I possessed a short-range radio, and it was this superior communications capability that went a long way to creating the stunning early German Blitzkrieg successes of 1939–41.

During 1935, production shifted to a slightly modified variant, the LaS IB (Sdkfz 101), based on the second Krupp-

ABOVE *The vehicles and two-man crews of a Panzer I unit line up for inspection after completing a training exercise. On the tanks' rear track guards are visible playing card insignia. Note also the white disk painted on the commander's turret hatch, presumably some kind of recognition device.*

produced prototype, the LKA2. This tank possessed a slightly elongated suspension with an extra fifth road wheel. The German Army had quickly recognised that the LaS IA tank was underpowered, and consequently the new LaS IB was driven by a more powerful 100bhp Maybach NL 38 TR engine that permitted an improved top road speed of 40kph (25mph). These modifications brought the weight of the LaS IB tank up to six tonnes (5.9 tons). The vehicle entered German service during 1935, and subsequently equipped the three panzer (armoured) divisions which were formed later that year.

Production Rates

Although the German Army had originally considered the LaS I as merely a stop-gap light training tank, a number of delays in the construction of the Panzer III and IV combat tanks meant that German factories completed far larger numbers of LaS IB tanks than was originally intended.

German firms continued to manufacture this tank over a five-year period between 1935 and 1939, constructing a total of 1500 vehicles at an average rate of 25 units per month. Between 1936 and 1939, both LaS I tank models were to see active service with the German Condor Legion alongside General Franco's Nationalist forces during the Spanish Civil War. In February 1938, with the need for subterfuge now at an end, the German High Command redesignated the LaS IA and IB tanks as the Panzer I Models A and B, respectively.

Late Development Projects

As the Panzer I neared the end of its production run in late 1939, German tank factories developed two new variants.

SPECIFICATIONS: Panzer I Model A (Sdkfz 101)

GENERAL
Vehicle Type: light training tank
Entered Service: mid-1934
Crew: two
Combat Weight: 5.4 tonnes (5.3 tons)

DIMENSIONS
Overall Length: 4.02m (13ft 2in)
Hull Length: 4.02m (13ft 2in)
Width: 2.06m (6ft 9in)
Height: 1.72m (5ft 8in)

ARMAMENT
Main: 2 x 7.92mm (0.312in)
MG 13 turret-mounted
Secondary: none

AMMUNITION STOWAGE
Main: 1525 rounds
Secondary: n/a

ARMOUR
Hull Front (Nose): 13mm (0.5in)
(at 63 degrees)
Hull Front (Driver's Plate): 13mm
(0.5in) (at 68 degrees)
Hull Sides: 13mm (0.5in)
(at 73 degrees- vertical)
Hull Rear: 13mm (0.5in)
(at 50-75 degrees)
Turret Front: 13mm (0.5in)
(at 80 degrees)
Turret Sides: 13mm (0.5in)
(at 68 degrees)

Turret Rear: 13mm (0.5in)
(at 68 degrees)
Turret Roof: 8mm (0.3in)
(at 0–18 degrees)

MOTIVE POWER
Engine: Krupp M305 B4-cylinder petrol
Power: 57 bhp
Fuel Capacity: 145 litres (32 gallons)

PERFORMANCE
Maximum Road Speed: 37kph (23mph)
Maximum Cross-Country Speed: n/k
Operational Range (Road): 145km
(90 miles)
Operational Range (Cross-Country):
97km (60 miles)

The Panzer I Model C (or VK601) air-portable light tank was intended to equip the newly formed German airborne division. The vehicle mounted the larger Panzer II turret with its 20mm gun on top of a modified Panzer I Model B chassis. This tank possessed heavier 30mm- (1.2in-) thick armour that increased the vehicle's weight to eight tonnes (7.9 tons). The Model C, however, was powered by a larger 150bhp Maybach HL 45 R6-cylinder engine that enabled the vehicle to achieve an impressive top road speed of 50kph (31mph), despite its increased weight.

In January 1941, the Army Weapons Department accepted the VK601 prototype and placed a pre-production order for 40 vehicles with the firm of Kraus Maffei, to be delivered by July 1942 – a generous 18 months in the future! Tactical developments and rapidly changing operational requirements, however, soon overtook this leisurely construction schedule, and Kraus Maffei completed only a few Model C pre-production vehicles before the German High Command cancelled the project in the summer of 1941.

BELOW *The five pairs of bogie wheels and the high-set idler identify this light tank as a Panzer I Model B. The very modest main armament of two MG 13 machine guns fundamentally undermined the tactical value of the Panzer I when in combat.*

The second version, the Panzer I Model D (VK1801) project, involved a heavily armoured variant of the Panzer I intended for the infantry close support role, in contravention of the German practice of concentrating all armour in the panzer divisions. The prototype design, completed by June 1940, mounted the standard Panzer I armament of twin machine guns, but was protected by much heavier 80mm- (3.2in-) thick armour that trebled the weight of the vehicle to 18 tonnes (17.7 tons). The light Panzer I chassis and the 150bhp Maybach HL 45 engine struggled with this greatly increased load, and thus the vehicle's top speed was reduced to a sluggish 25kph (15mph) by road, and even less over rough terrain. Field trials soon revealed that the design was too heavy for its chassis, and subsequently the German Army rejected the development of tanks for use in infantry support roles. Consequently, the Weapons Department cancelled the project after German factories had completed just 12 vehicles from a pre-production order of 30 units. The German Army employed these 12 Panzer I Model D tanks on the Eastern Front in an infantry support role.

Specialised Variants

The German Army also produced several specialised variants of the standard Panzer I tank. These included the

ABOVE *This view of the Panzer I Model A illustrates well the octagonal central hull superstructure on which the turret is mounted. The hull itself was lightly armoured and had many openings and crevices which made it vulnerable to attack.*

Model A(fl) and B(fl) flame-throwing tanks that mounted a flame-thrower device instead of the tank's right-hand turret machine gun. German firms also constructed 200 Kleiner Panzerbefehlswagen I (Sdkfz 165) command tanks between 1934 and 1937. Three different versions of this vehicle were produced, most of which had their turrets replaced with a better-protected fixed superstructure that mounted a single machine gun in the hull front for close defence. The crew of the Panzer I command tank was increased to three by the addition of a radio operator to work the sophisticated communications that the vehicle carried. The High Command allocated these command vehicles to the headquarters platoons of panzer battalions, where they remained in service until replaced by more modern command vehicles in late 1942.

Given the unexpected delay in Panzer III and IV production, Germany entered World War II in the unenviable position of possessing an armoured force based largely on Panzer I and II light training tanks. For its invasion of Poland in September 1939, no less than one-third of the German panzer force – some 1445 vehicles – were Panzer I tanks armed just with machine guns. Indeed, the German Army was forced to rely heavily on the limited combat power of the Panzer I and II throughout its first year of

spectacular Blitzkrieg successes. Between mid-1940 and early 1941, however, the German Army either relegated most of the remaining 800 Panzer I tanks – now obsolete as combat vehicles – to training or garrison duties in Nazi-occupied Europe, or converted them into various support vehicles. In fact, the only Panzer I vehicles to see active frontline service after late 1941 were a few flame-throwing tank variants deployed in North Africa.

Support Vehicles

The German Army converted many of its Panzer I tanks into a range of support vehicles. Back in mid-1939, the firm of Alkett had already converted 38 Panzer I Model B tanks into the SiG 33 improvised heavy infantry self-propelled gun. This 8.5-tonne (8.4-ton) vehicle mounted a 15cm heavy infantry gun in a tall box-shaped superstructure fitted on top of the Panzer I tank chassis. In late 1939, German factories had also converted 51 Panzer I tanks into munitions carriers by removing their turrets.

During 1940 other Panzer I tanks had their turrets and superstructures removed to create the Driver Training Vehicle I, many of which served with the paramilitary National Socialist Motor Corps. In that same year, German firms also converted further tanks into Bergepanzer I recovery vehicles, used to rescue disabled tanks from the battlefield, or into ramp-carrying vehicles, designated the Bruckenleger I. More significantly, during spring 1941 German factories converted 132 Panzer I Model B tanks into Panzerjäger I (Sdkfz 101) light self-propelled anti-tank guns.

These vehicles mounted a Czech 4.7cm Pak 36(t) L/43 gun in a lightly armoured, three-sided shield fitted on top of the Panzer I chassis. During Operation 'Barbarossa', the Germans deployed all of these vehicles in infantry division anti-tank battalions, as their only effective mobile anti-tank weapon.

Panzer I in Combat

The first opportunity for the German Army to test its LaS IA and IB light tanks occurred during the 1936–39 Spanish Civil War. Germany supplied equipment and volunteers in the form of the Condor Legion to aid Franco's Nationalist forces in their war against the Republicans. The Legion employed 120 LaS tanks in Colonel Ritter von Thoma's armoured group. During the Civil War the German Army gained invaluable combat experience with the LaS tank, although this experience also underscored the vehicle's obvious tactical shortcomings – its limited firepower and protection. To rectify the tank's lack of an effective main armament, Spanish workshops modified a few Panzer I tanks to mount a more potent 20mm cannon, although this upgrading resulted in a markedly reduced cross-country performance.

The Panzer I constituted a major part of the German panzer division establishment on the eve of the Polish Campaign. Although the German Army's premier fighting formation – the 1st Panzer Division – fielded just 68 Panzer I tanks, the 2nd–5th Panzer Divisions each deployed 136 Panzer I tanks out of a total establishment of 328 vehicles. Given that only 98 Panzer III medium and 211 Panzer IV medium/heavy tanks could be utilised in the campaign, German success consequently rested principally with the 1445 Panzer I and 1223 Panzer II light tanks that were employed. The stunning German success in Poland, therefore, was more the product of the German Army's tactical excellence than it was of superiority in the armoured fighting vehicles it fielded.

Vulnerability of the Panzer I

Despite the German success in Poland, the vulnerability of the lightly armoured Panzer I tank to Polish 37mm anti-tank rounds soon became apparent. The very limited firepower of the Panzer I also meant that it needed the support of heavier German tanks to defeat even light Polish tankettes. Moreover, the campaign demonstrated that the Panzer I, despite its modest weight, often became bogged down in muddy terrain, this being particularly evident during the

BELOW *A Panzer I Model B command vehicle. Note the field-grey camouflage and the large white cross national markings painted on this vehicle. These distinguishing marks were common in pre-war German armoured fighting vehicles.*

Polish counter-attack along the River Bzura. The fact that in Poland 89 Panzer I tanks were lost out of a total German tank casualty figure of 219 vehicles indicates both how heavily the Germans relied on this tank and how vulnerable it proved to enemy fire. A significant proportion of these Panzer I casualties occurred in the ruins of Warsaw, where determined Polish resistance took a steady toll of the light armour that the Germans unwisely committed to combat in confined urban back streets.

Successes in the Frontline

Given the rugged mountainous terrain, the German invasion of Norway in April 1940 (Operation 'Weser Exercise') was not a Blitzkrieg-style armoured warfare campaign. However, the Germans employed limited amounts of armour to support their invasion, deploying 50 tanks in the specially raised 40th Panzer Battalion. The armour, including two dozen Panzer I vehicles, played a crucial role in breaching the Anglo-French blocking force deployed across the narrow floor of the Gubrandsdalen Valley. The success of this armoured thrust forced the Anglo-French expeditionary force which had arrived in the Namsos-Aandalsnes area on 17 April to retreat hastily to its landing zones for naval evacuation back to Britain on 3 May 1940.

Between the end of the Polish Campaign and the German invasion of the West in May 1940, the German Army reorganised its panzer forces. The High Command converted its four light divisions into the 6th–9th Panzer Divisions and completed the raising of a tenth panzer division. Some 1077 Panzer I tanks remained in service with the German Army in May 1940 – 348 less than in September 1939, thanks to the loss of 89 vehicles in the Polish Campaign and the conversion of 261 tanks for various specialised roles. The German Army, however, only employed 619 Panzer I tanks in its invasion of the West, utilising the remaining 458 vehicles for either training purposes or garrison duties.

The fighting in the West served to confirm the German Army's concern that the Panzer I would be no match for French tanks in combat. The Germans used Panzer I command tanks in their headquarters units, and increasingly employed their standard Panzer I tanks solely in a reconnaissance or scouting role. Losses among the latter vehicles, however, were heavy whenever they engaged Anglo-French armour, and consequently after May 1940 the Germans never again employed the Panzer I as a frontline combat tank.

CHAPTER 2

PANZER II

Another stop-gap training tank, the Panzer II was designed to swell the ranks of the German armoured divisions until the Panzer III and IV combat tanks entered service. Indeed, despite its limitations, it formed the backbone of the German Army's armoured divisions, and as late as April 1942, a total of 860 were still on strength.

The Panzer II was a heavier version of the light Panzer I training tank, which was ordered by the German Army in the early 1930s as a stop-gap until the main combat tanks (the Panzer III and IV) appeared in the later years of that decade. In July 1934, the Army Weapons Department put out to tender the design specifications for a 10-tonne (9.8-ton) vehicle mounting a 2cm gun in a fully traversing turret. Three firms submitted designs, and the Weapons Department selected the Augsburg-Nuremburg Machine Works (MAN) project for a limited pre-production run. Between 1935 and 1937, MAN completed several series of prototype and pre-production vehicles under the camouflage designation Agricultural

LEFT Four Panzer II Model D tanks carefully drive up mobile ramps onto their transport lorries. The suspension of the Panzer II was radically different from that of its predecessor, in that it was based on large bogie wheels.

Tractor 100 (LaS 100). In 1938, when such deception was no longer necessary, the German Army redesignated this tank as the Panzer II.

Development History

The first pre-production model was the la/LaS 100 (Panzer II Model a1), of which MAN constructed 11 vehicles in 1935. The German Army designated Panzer II production variants with capital letters in the normal manner but, rather unusually, identified pre-production models with a lower-case letter. A 130bhp R6-cylinder Maybach HL 57 engine powered the Model a1. The tank's suspension was based on six road wheels connected by a girder beam, attached to the hull by three leaf springs. This variant was identifiable by a highly rounded hull nose plate. The Model a1 weighed 7.5 tonnes (7.4 tons), possessed armour that was 14.5mm- (0.6in-) thick, and mounted as its main armament the 2cm KwK 30 L/55 gun. This weapon was a 20mm tank gun

introduced in 1930 (hence KwK 30) which possessed a barrel length of 55 calibres, that is, 55 times longer than the gun's diameter (hence L/55). Subsequently, during 1935 MAN constructed 25 Panzer II Model a2 tanks, identical to their predecessors except for minor changes to the engine compartment. Further minor modifications to the cooling system and suspension produced the third Panzer II pre-production variant, the Model a3, some 50 of which entered German service during 1936.

The next pre-production version to enter service, also during 1936, was the 2/LaS 100 or Panzer II Model b. This tank incorporated a more powerful engine, the 140bhp Maybach HL 62 TRM, which raised the vehicle's weight to 7.9 tonnes (7.8 tons). Observers could easily distinguish the Model b from its predecessors by an angular hull nose that replaced the distinctive rounded cone which characterised both the earlier pre-production variants and the subsequent production Model A–C tanks. German firms completed 100 Model b tanks during 1936–37. Commencing during 1937

ABOVE *A column of Panzer II tanks parade through the streets before a packed throng of onlookers. The vehicle in the foreground, II3, is the third vehicle of the staff company in the 2nd Battalion of this unidentified Panzer division.*

with the Model c, the last pre-production variant, the Germans introduced fundamental design changes. This vehicle featured a redesigned suspension with five large road wheels hung from quarter-elliptic springs, a format that would be used throughout the rest of the Panzer II production run. This and other modifications increased significantly the weight of the Model c to 8.9 tonnes (8.8 tons). Mass production commenced with the 4/LaS 100 or Panzer II Model A in 1937, which differed from its predecessor merely in featuring a redesigned driver's visor. During 1937–38, the slightly modified Model B entered service. Next, during 1938–39, German firms produced the Model C vehicle that incorporated a better protected driver's vision port.

The Panzer II Models D and E marked a radical departure from their predecessors. In 1938 Daimler-Benz received contracts to produce a fast tank variant of the Panzer II to equip the German Army's four light divisions for use in classic cavalry reconnaissance roles.

The Model D and E tanks possessed a redesigned hull superstructure which now incorporated scaled-down components of the Panzer III tank that Daimler-Benz was then also producing. Most significantly, these fast tanks possessed modified tracks and a novel torsion bar suspension in order to increase their maximum road speed to an impressive 56kph (35mph). Some 250 of these Panzer II fast tanks entered German service during 1938–39, but they failed to live up to German expectations, principally due to poor cross-country performance. During 1939, the German Army modified 90 of these unsatisfactory vehicles to produce the Flammpanzer II Flamingo flamethrower tank and converted the remainder during 1942 into Marder II tank destroyers.

During the September 1939 invasion of Poland, the 1223 Panzer II tanks deployed by the German Army formed the mainstay of its armoured forces. In fact, in early 1939 the Germans had decided that there were sufficient numbers of

this tank type in service and consequently scaled down its production. German firms produced just 15 new Panzer II tanks during 1939 and only nine in 1940. The tactical lessons which the German Army derived from the Polish Campaign also prompted this virtual halt to new construction. The Germans concluded that the Panzer II was insufficiently gunned and protected, and consequently reduced new construction in order to concentrate on up-armouring many of the 1200 Panzer II tanks already in service. Hence, during the winter of 1939–40, German factories fitted many early models with additional 20mm- (0.8in-) thick armour plates onto the vehicle's original 14.5mm (0.6in) frontal armour. German firms also retro-fitted early models with more resilient angular nose plates to replace the original curved hull nose. Another retrospective modification carried out by German factories during the summer of 1940 involved the conversion of 50 Panzer II vehicles into submersible tanks, designated Schwimmpanzer II. The German Army intended

BELOW *Side view of a Panzer II Model L Luchs (Lynx), which was subsequently reclassified as an armed reconnaissance vehicle. Note the fundamentally redesigned suspension that enabled the Luchs to reach very impressive speeds both by road and across country.*

to use these vehicles for Operation 'Sealion', its planned invasion of Britain.

The Final Product Variant

Significant new construction of the Panzer II did not recommence until March 1941 when work began on the final production variant, the Model F. German firms designed this new model with the benefit of the experience gained in the campaigns against Norway and France during April–June 1940. The performance of the Panzer II in these campaigns again highlighted the need for improved levels of protection. Consequently, the Model F possessed frontal armour that consisted of a single homogeneous 35mm (1.4in) plate, together with enhanced side armour of 30mm- (1.2in-) thickness. This improved protection raised the tank's weight to 9.5 tonnes (9.3 tons), with a corresponding reduction in maximum speed to 40kph (25mph).

The lessons the Germans derived from Operation 'Barbarossa', their June 1941 onslaught against the Soviet Union, soon made it clear that the Panzer II was nearing the end of its active life. The vehicle's turret ring was too small to mount a sufficiently powerful main armament, and the chassis could not bear the weight of the levels of armour protection needed for combat on the Eastern Front in late 1941. However, the Germans continued to produce the Panzer II Model F well into 1942, despite its growing obsolescence. Hitler's decision in the summer of 1941 to expand the panzer force to 36 divisions meant that a huge increase in production was required. The Germans found it expedient to continue producing established vehicles, which they could mass-produce cheaply, rather than suffer the inevitable decline in delivery rates associated with switching to the construction of newly developed tanks. During 1941, German factories produced 233 Panzer II Model F tanks, and during 1942 they constructed a further 306 Model G and J vehicles. These new variants were identifiable by the external stowage bin fitted at the rear of their turrets. But on the Eastern Front during 1942, even these latest Panzer II models were scarcely fit for frontline combat and consequently the Germans employed the Panzer II increasingly as a reconnaissance vehicle rather than as a battle tank.

As the German Army gradually phased the Panzer II out of frontline service from late 1942, it used the tank's reliable chassis as a platform for various other armoured fighting vehicles. During 1942–43, German firms produced 1983 Marder II self-propelled guns of all types on the Panzer II chassis. Similarly, during 1943–44, some 683 Panzer II

chassis formed the basis for an armoured self-propelled artillery vehicle called the Wespe (Wasp) which mounted the 10.5cm Light Field Howitzer 18/1. Finally, during 1944–45 German factories stripped obsolete Panzer II tanks of their turrets to produce 158 munitions carriers for use with Wespe-equipped artillery batteries.

Panzer II in Combat

The high casualty rates sustained among the 1223 Panzer II tanks deployed in Poland attest to the great reliance that the German Army placed on this tank. According to German statistics, Polish forces knocked out 81 Panzer II tanks, but only a further 141 vehicles among all the other five tank types that the Germans deployed. The largest loss of Panzer II tanks occurred on 8–9 September 1939 in Warsaw's

SPECIFICATIONS: Panzer II Model F (Sdkfz121)

GENERAL
Vehicle Type: light tank
Entered Service: spring 1941
Crew: three
Combat Weight: 9.5 tonnes (9.3 tons)

DIMENSIONS
Overall Length: 4.81m (15ft 9in)
Hull Length: 4.81m (15ft 9in)
Width: 2.28m (7ft 6in)
Height: 2.02m (6ft 7in)

ARMAMENT
Main: 2cm (0.8in) KwK 30 (or KwK 38) L/55 gun
Secondary: 2 x 7.92mm (0.312in) MG 34; 1 coaxial in turret; 1 hull front.

AMMUNITION STOWAGE
Main: 180 rounds
Secondary: 2550 rounds

ARMOUR
Hull Front (Nose): 35mm (1.4in) (at 77 degrees)
Hull Front (Driver's Plate): 30mm (1.2in) (at 80 degrees)
Hull Sides: 20mm (0.8in) (at 90 degrees)
Hull Rear: 14.5mm (0.6in) (at 90 degrees)
Turret Front: 30mm (1.2in) (at 90 degrees)
Turret Sides: 15mm (0.6in) (at 68 degrees)
Turret Rear: 14.5mm (0.6in) (at 68 degrees)

Turret Roof: 10mm (0.4in) (at 0–13 degrees)

MOTIVE POWER
Engine: Maybach HL 62 TRM R6-cylinder petrol
Power: 140 bhp
Fuel Capacity: 170 litres (30.81 gallons)

PERFORMANCE
Maximum Road Speed: 40kph (25mph)
Maximum Cross-Country Speed: 19kph (12mph)
Operational Range (Road): 200km (124 miles)
Operational Range (Cross-Country): 130km (81 miles)

suburbs. German commanders unwisely rushed the light armour of the 4th Panzer Division into the city's back streets with inadequate infantry support, and consequently Polish forces knocked out 32 Panzer II tanks. It was in Warsaw that the Germans first discovered the considerable risk that fighting in built-up areas posed to armoured forces.

The next action in which Panzer II vehicles participated was the German invasion of Norway. Given the rugged Norwegian terrain, German armour played a less fundamental role here than it had done in Poland. Nevertheless, the German Army deployed the specially raised 40th Panzer Battalion with 50 tanks on strength – including 16 Panzer II vehicles – to provide fire support for German infantry units. This battalion participated in the German combined-arms attack launched against the Anglo-French expeditionary force in the Gubrandsdalen Valley north of Lillehammer. Despite losing two Panzer II tanks to British anti-tank fire, this German assault successfully forced the Anglo-French troops to retreat back to their landing zones for naval evacuation.

By the time of the German invasion of the West in May 1940, the German Army clearly recognised that the Panzer II was now a vehicle of limited tactical value, suitable only for reconnaissance and flank protection duties in support of the more formidable Panzer 38(t), III and IV tanks. This realisation was reflected in the force composition of the panzer divisions that had been committed to the invasion of the West. The German High Command allocated greater numbers of Panzer III and IV tanks and fewer Panzer I and II light tanks to those panzer divisions undertaking the main thrust through the Ardennes than it did to those divisions with less central missions. For example, the three panzer divisions in General Heinz Guderian's spearhead XIX Panzer Corps, for example, each deployed 146 Panzer III and IV tanks, but only 130 light Panzer I and II tanks. In contrast, the High Command allotted the 9th Panzer Division just 54 Panzer III and IV vehicles in addition to 175 light tanks for the less crucial mission of undertaking a feint into Holland.

Although in this campaign the Panzer II had limited value in tank-versus-tank engagements due to its modest main armament and inadequate protection, it still possessed two advantages over French armour that offset these weaknesses. First, since the Panzer II (like other German tanks) possessed a two-man turret crew, it achieved a higher rate of fire than did French tanks with their one-man turret crews. Second, as every Panzer II (like all German tanks) possessed a short-range radio, cooperation within the panzer divisions outclassed that within French armoured

formations. In France, the German Army enjoyed neither quantitative nor qualitative advantage in armoured fighting vehicles. But the Germans achieved success through better tactical coordination within their panzer regiments and superior cooperation between all arms and services, especially with the Stuka dive-bombers of the German Air Force (Luftwaffe).

Despite its frailties, the Panzer II still remained a common tank during Operation 'Barbarossa'. But bitter fighting on the Eastern Front further highlighted the rapidly decreasing tactical value of the Panzer II. Used mainly for

ABOVE *A column of Panzer tanks advances through a French town during the stunning successes of the German Blitzkrieg in the West in May 1940. The relatively small size of this tank is evident in comparison with the height of its crew.*

reconnaissance, the tank suffered heavy losses whenever it engaged newer Soviet tanks and anti-tank guns. Both combat losses and redeployment to reserve duties meant that by late 1942 the Panzer II was a rare vehicle in frontline service. Only in North Africa was this scarcity noticeably absent, since equipment shortages denied General Erwin Rommel's Africa Corps the luxury of discarding its tactically limited Panzer II tanks until more modern equipment had arrived. In May 1942, for example, during the battle for Tobruk, Rommel's force of 560 tanks still included 50 Panzer II vehicles. By the time of General Montgomery's great

British offensive at El Alamein in October 1942, the Africa Corps still deployed 31 old Panzer II tanks in its inventory of 520 German and Italian tanks. By early 1943, however, the German Army had redeployed all its remaining 300 Panzer II tanks from frontline service to garrison or anti-partisan duties in various parts of Nazi-occupied Europe.

CHAPTER 3

MARDER I

The German Army's desperate need to improve its anti-tank capability led it from 1942 to develop a series of self-propelled guns called Marder that utilised captured guns or chassis. The first such vehicle, the Marder I, mounted a powerful German gun on the captured French Lorraine Schlepper chassis.

After their rapid conquest of France in May–June 1940, the Germans captured hundreds of intact British and French tanks and other armoured fighting vehicles. Among the most valuable of these vehicles was the French Lorraine carrier, a fully tracked armoured chassis that the French had used both to transport infantry and as an artillery tractor. Its powerful engine and stability quickly impressed the Germans, who designated the vehicle the Lorraine Schlepper. After the Germans encountered large numbers of Soviet medium T34 and heavy KV1 tanks during the early stages of Operation 'Barbarossa', they realised that they urgently needed more powerful and mobile anti-tank capability. Consequently, the German Army

LEFT *The destructive Marder I self-propelled gun utilised the unusual suspended chassis of the Lorraine Schlepper with its three pairs of bogie wheels. Note also the gun shield fitted over the vehicle's armoured fighting compartment.*

looked around for suitable chassis on which to mount a variety of anti-tank guns, to create improvised light tank-destroyers while awaiting the design of purpose-built ones. In the course of this search, the Germans naturally turned to the large stock of captured French vehicles in their possession, and in particular the Lorraine carrier, which they soon realised made a suitable chassis for a variety of specialised vehicles.

Development History

The improvised tank destroyer that the Germans produced, based on the Lorraine Schlepper chassis, became known as the Marder (Marten) I, the first of a series of Marder armoured fighting vehicles that utilised captured main armaments and/or chassis. The mastermind behind the Marder I was Alfred Becker, a German engineer from the Alfred Becker firm of Krefeld. During the 1940 campaign in the West, Captain Becker served as an artillery battery

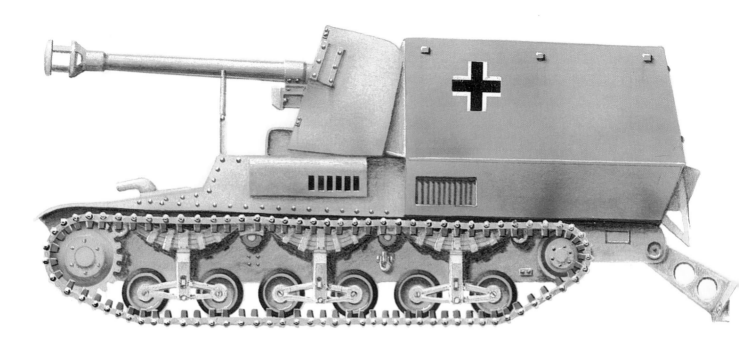

SPECIFICATIONS: Panzerjäger Marder I (Sdkfz 135)

GENERAL
Vehicle Type: light tank destroyer
(self-propelled anti-tank gun)
Entered Service: summer 1942
Crew: four
Combat Weight: 8.3 tonnes
(8.2 tons)
Chassis: French Lorraine Schlepper
gun carriage

DIMENSIONS
Overall Length: 5.38m (17ft)
Hull Length: 4.35m (14ft 3in)
Width: 1.88m (6ft 2in)
Height: 2.00m (6ft 7in)

ARMAMENT
Main: 7.5cm (3in) PaK 40/1 L/46 gun

Main Gun Traverse: 24 degrees left to
24 degrees right
Secondary: none

AMMUNITION STOWAGE
Main: 40 rounds
Secondary: n/a

ARMOUR
Hull Front (Nose): 12mm (0.5in)
(at 78 degrees)
Hull Front (Driver's Plate): 12mm
(0.5in) (at 90 degrees)
Hull Sides: 9mm (0.35in) (at 75–90 degrees)
Hull Rear: 9mm (0.35in) (at 80 degrees)
Superstructure Front: 12mm (0.5in)
(at 80 degrees)
Superstructure Sides: 9mm (0.35in)

(at 75 degrees)
Superstructure Rear: 9mm (0.35in)
(at 74 degrees)
Superstructure Roof: none

MOTIVE POWER
Engine: De La Haye 103 TT R6-cylinder
petrol
Power: 70 bhp
Fuel Capacity: 111 litres (24 gallons)

PERFORMANCE
Maximum Speed (Road): 38kph
(21mph)
Operational Range (Road): 150km
(93 miles)
Operational Range (Cross-Country):
90km (56 miles)

commander in the 227th Infantry Division. He proved to be an officer of great initiative, energy and creativity, and as his division advanced through the Netherlands, he motorised his horse-drawn artillery battery by utilising captured Dutch motor vehicles. After the successful conquest of the West, the 227th Infantry Division remained in France on occupation duties, during which time Captain Becker constructed improvised self-propelled artillery vehicles by marrying captured artillery pieces with vehicle chassis. The result was the first self-propelled artillery to see service with the German Army.

Although his division's transfer to the Eastern Front, to participate in the invasion of the Soviet Union, cramped

Becker's ingenuity, his enterprise finally caught the attention of higher authorities. During the summer of 1942, the German High Command seconded Becker to the Alkett firm at Berlin-Spandau, which dispatched him to France to oversee the conversion of French vehicles into specialised armoured fighting vehicles for German service. The Army Weapons Department placed Becker in charge of a construction staff and workshop in Paris, with instructions to convert sufficient vehicles to equip two entire armoured divisions. Becker combed French military depots, collecting vehicles, chassis and spare parts and, during 1942-43, hundreds of conversions were made by Alkett, by the Becker concern and by various French factories.

Becker's return to France coincided with an order from the Weapons Department of 25 May 1942 for the development of the Lorraine Schlepper as a self-propelled mount for German anti-tank and artillery guns. Some 160 carriers were earmarked for conversion, including 60 as the basis for improvised tank destroyers that mounted the new German 7.5cm Pak 40 heavy anti-tank gun. On 4 June 1942, verification that a further 78 Lorraine carriers were under repair at the army motor vehicle park at Bielitz led Field Marshal Keitel to order a further 24 carriers refurbished as platforms for this gun. The vehicle was officially designated the 7.5cm Pak 40/1 auf Geschützwagen Lorraine Schlepper (f) (Sdkfz 135), or the 7.5cm 1940 anti-tank gun on the French Lorraine Carrier gun carriage. The vehicle became commonly known as the Marder I. During June–July 1942 the Germans completed 104 Marder I conversions, followed by another 66 in August 1942 and a further 15 by the end of the year, for a total production run of 185 vehicles. Of this total, 48 conversions took place at the Alkett works, others at the Alfred Becker firm at Krefeld, and the remainder in France, including some in Paris, where the Lorraine carriers themselves were renovated.

The Marder I self-propelled anti-tank gun was distinguishable from its cousins, the Marder II and III, by its suspended chassis which had six small 445mm (17.5in) rubber-tyred bogie wheels on each side, sprung in three pairs on semi-elliptical leaf springs, an unusual wheel arrangement. The driving sprocket was at the front. The track-adjusting idler was mounted at the rear and supported by four return rollers, which were located at the ends of the suspension springs. The carrier was fitted with wide, 100mm (3.9in) tracks that provided good stability and traction. On the basic armoured chassis of the Lorraine carrier, above the vehicle's original passenger compartment, the Germans constructed a high, box-like, open-topped superstructure, with minimal armament that sloped to the rear.

The 7.5cm Pak 40 anti-tank gun was mounted with its front shield fitted directly over this superstructure frame, which consequently limited its horizontal traverse. The main armament had a vertical elevation of between -5 degrees and +22 degrees. The long 3.5m (11ft 6in) barrel overhung the front of the vehicle and necessitated the fitting of a barrel rest on the front hull to support the gun during long-distance travel. The performance of the main armament was good: it possessed a muzzle velocity of 549 metres per second (1800 feet per second) firing high-explosive rounds and 770 m/s (2525 f/s) firing armour-piercing shot. Its high muzzle velocity ensured that the gun could penetrate an impressive 91mm (3.6in) of 30-degree sloped armour at 914m (2998ft).

The Marder I could only be lightly armoured, however, in order to keep the vehicle's weight down to 8.3 tonnes (7.2 tons) and avoid overloading the chassis. Armour protection was a mere 12mm (0.5in) on the cast front plate and 9mm (0.35in) on the pressed steel sides and rear, only sufficient to protect against small-arms fire. The four-man vehicle was powered by a 70bhp De La Haye 103TT R6-cylinder petrol engine that gave a maximum speed of 38kph (21mph). The vehicle possessed a 111 litre (24 gallon) fuel tank, plus an additional 25 litre (5.5 gallon) reserve tank that provided an operational range of between 90 and 150km (56 and 93 miles), depending on the terrain.

The Marder I in Combat

The vehicle served principally with German occupation forces in France, in the anti-tank battalions of infantry divisions. Small numbers saw service on the Eastern Front and in Italy during 1943–44, after their parent divisions were transferred from the Western theatre. Most Marder I vehicles, however, remained in France and 131 were still in service there on 1 January 1944. During the previous year, the German Army had consolidated the various improvised armoured fighting vehicles in its possession which were designed and constructed by Alfred Becker, into the 931st Mobile Brigade West, a formation that soon became the backbone of the meagre German strategic reserve then stationed in the West.

After the destruction of the 21st Panzer Division in Tunisia in May 1943, the German High Command ordered that the division be reconstituted in Normandy, using the Mobile Brigade West. The recently promoted Major Becker took command of the rebuilt 21st Panzer Division's 200th Assault Gun Battalion, which fielded 45 Marder I tank destroyers in five batteries, making it the largest unit to be equipped with the vehicle.

Major Becker commanded this battalion throughout the 1944 Normandy campaign, where these improvised tank destroyers, despite their insufficient armour protection, proved to be very effective. Indeed, the Marder I acquitted itself well in combat against Anglo-American tanks in Normandy. On 2 July 1944, Major Becker was awarded the coveted Knight's Cross for his valiant and effective command of the 200th Battalion during the bitter fighting for Caen. The energetic resistance put up by Becker's unit helped to deny the surrender of this city to General Montgomery's Anglo-Canadian forces throughout June 1944.

CHAPTER 4

MARDER II

The second vehicle in the Marder series of improvised tank destroyers married the potent captured Soviet 7.62cm gun to the reliable Panzer II chassis. When stocks of this weapon had been exhausted the Germans mounted their own 7.5cm gun in later Marder II vehicles. The Marder II remained in service until the end of the war, serving on all fronts.

The German Army's need for greater and more mobile anti-tank firepower to counter modern Red Army tanks in the wake of Germany's invasion of the Soviet Union, led to the emergence of a series of improvised tank destroyers, which mounted powerful anti-tank weapons. The Germans naturally turned to the solid and dependable chassis of the Panzer II tank as a platform for such an expedient anti-tank vehicle. Consequently, during the spring of 1942 the firm of Alkett designed a vehicle that married the Panzer II chassis to the only available weapon then capable of penetrating the frontal armour of the Soviet T34 and KV1 tanks. Ironically, this weapon happened to be the Red Army's own 7.62cm M36

LEFT The first version of the Marder II, the 7.62cm-gunned (Sdkfz), mounted the potent Soviet weapon in a gun shield fitted on top of a tall, box-like superstructure constructed on the Panzer II chassis. The result was a vehicle with a very high silhouette.

field gun, which the Germans had captured in large numbers during the opening stages of Operation 'Barbarossa'.

Development History

This improvised tank destroyer mounted a German-modified version of the Soviet 7.62cm gun on the Panzer II Model D and E tank chassis. German workshops rechambered the Soviet weapon so that it fired the anti-tank round used with the new German 7.5cm Pak 40/2 anti-tank gun. The Germans designated this modified gun the 7.62cm Pak 36(r). A few of these tank destroyers, however, mounted unmodified Soviet field guns, designated the 7.62cm FK 296(r). Back in 1938, Daimler-Benz had designed the Panzer II Models D and E as fast tanks for reconnaissance missions with the four German light divisions. These tanks, however, proved a disappointment: their novel suspension delivered a poor cross-country performance, while the light division concept proved a failure in Poland. By 1941, therefore, these tanks had become redundant and thus were available for conversion. The German Army officially designated this self-propelled anti-tank gun as the Panzerjäger II Ausf D-E für 7.62cm Pak 36(r) (Sdkfz 132). Hitler subsequently conferred the name Marder (Marten) II on the vehicle, and it was by this name that the vehicle was commonly known. Alkett converted 185 Panzer II Model D and E tanks during late spring 1942, including 30 vehicles previously converted into the Flammpanzer II Flamingo flamethrower tank.

Alkett effected the conversion by removing the original Panzer II turret and superstructure and replacing it with a high, box-like, 14.5mm- (0.6in-) thick armoured superstructure with steeply sloping sides. The main armament was mounted centrally on top of this superstructure within a three-sided gun shield of 10mm- (0.4in-) thickness, the entire gun being bolted onto the inside of the lower superstructure. The long 4.2m (13ft 9in) barrel of the 7.62cm gun overhung the front of the chassis, and the entire upper-shield section traversed with the main armament. The crew elevated the gun by hand

SPECIFICATIONS: Panzerjäger Marder II (Sdkfz 132)

GENERAL
Vehicle Type: light tank destroyer (self-propelled anti-tank gun)
Entered Service: spring 1942
Crew: four
Combat Weight: 10.7 tonnes (10.5 tons)
Chassis: Panzer II

DIMENSIONS
Overall Length: 4.88m (16 ft)
Hull Length: 4.64m (15ft 3in)
Width: 2.3m (7ft 6in)
Height: 2.65m (8t 8in)

ARMAMENT
Main: 7.6cm (3in) Pak 36(r) gun
Main Gun Traverse: 33 degrees left to 32 degrees right

Secondary: none

AMMUNITION STOWAGE
Main: 30 rounds
Secondary: n/a

ARMOUR
Hull Front (Nose): 30mm (1.2in) (at 78 degrees)
Hull Front (Driver's Plate): 30mm (1.2in) (at 90 degrees)
Hull Sides: 15mm (0.6in) (at 90 degrees)
Hull Rear: 8mm (0.3in) (at 90 degrees)
Superstructure Front: 15mm (0.6in) (at 62 degrees)
Superstructure Sides: 15mm (0.6in) (at 84 degrees)

Superstructure Rear: none
Superstructure Roof: none

MOTIVE POWER
Engine: Maybach HL 62 TRM R6-cylinder petrol
Power: 140 bhp
Fuel Capacity: 200 litres (44 gallons)

PERFORMANCE
Maximum Speed (Road): 45km (28mph)
Maximum Speed (Cross-Country): 19km (12mph)
Operational Range (Road): 185km (115 miles)
Operational Range (Cross-Country): 121km (75 miles)

through a range of between -5 degrees and +22 degrees, although the lower superstructure restricted the gun's field of horizontal traverse to just 65 degrees.

The powerful Soviet 76.2mm gun possessed a muzzle velocity of 551 metres per second (1805 feet per second) firing high-explosive and 797 m/s (2430 f/s) firing armour-piercing rounds. The latter could penetrate 81mm (3.2in) of armour sloped at 30 degrees and 104mm (4.1in) of vertical armour at a range of 914m (2998ft). This impressive anti-tank performance was more than sufficient to tackle any tank in service in 1942. The vehicle's lethal firepower, however, was offset by its modest level of armour protection. The 10–14.5mm- (0.4–0.6in-) thick frontal and side armour could withstand little more than small-arms fire, while the fighting compartment (the lower superstructure) remained open at the rear, leaving the crew vulnerable to enemy fire.

This modest level of protection was necessary to offset the larger and heavier gun that the vehicle carried in comparison with the small 2cm cannon mounted in the standard Panzer II tank. Despite its light armour, the Marder II still weighed 10.7 tonnes (10.5 tons) – close to the effective load limit of the standard Panzer II chassis powered by the 140bhp Maybach HL 62 TRM R6-cylinder engine. Both weight considerations and space limitations ensured that the vehicle could only carry 30 rounds for its main armament, a drawback that limited the tactical employment of this four-man operated vehicle.

After converting all of the 185 available Panzer II Model D and E tanks, Alkett completed another 50 Marder II vehicles on the chassis of the Panzer II Model F. During late 1942, the German Army employed these 235 vehicles in infantry division anti-tank battalions on the Eastern Front. Here the 7.62cm-gunned Marder II (Sdkfz 132) quickly proved popular with German troops thanks to the much needed powerful anti-tank punch that it provided.

The success of the Marder II tank destroyer led to additional construction orders and, from mid-1942, Alkett began converting large numbers of Panzer II Model A–C tanks into a modified version of the tank destroyer. These vehicles mounted either the unmodified 7.62cm Soviet FK 296(r) field gun (without muzzle brake) or the rechambered 7.62cm Pak 36(r) (with muzzle brake) on top of the basic Panzer II chassis. In this Marder II variant, however, the gun was mounted within a single section, lightly armoured, three-sided shield fitted directly on to the chassis, leaving the fighting compartment open at both the top and rear. This vehicle's silhouette was markedly different from the original Marder II design, mainly due to both its lack of a box-like lower-superstructure and the addition of a cradle fitted to the hull

front, to support the long, overhanging gun barrel during long journeys. This modified Marder II variant was officially designated the Panzerjäger II Ausf A–C für 7.62cm Pak 36(r) (Sdkfz 131). During 1942–43, Alkett converted 531 obsolete Panzer II tanks into 7.62cm Marder II (Sdkfz 131) self-propelled guns. The German Army issued these vehicles to the anti-tank battalions of both panzer and infantry divisions.

The Marder II in Combat

The Germans employed the Marder II principally on the Eastern Front with infantry anti-tank battalions where it proved a valuable addition to towed German anti-tank guns. The vehicle also served in the East with the anti-tank battalions of mechanised divisions, as well as in a few independent self-propelled anti-tank units. During 1942–43, the Marder II and its cousin, the Marder III, were the only effective German mobile anti-tank weapons available to counter Soviet armour. The Western Allies did not encounter the vehicle until early 1943 in Tunisia. Their forces soon learned to have a healthy respect for the heavy anti-tank punch of the Marder II, particularly after encountering it regularly during the 1944 Italian campaign. The purpose-built Jagdpanzer 38(t) light tank destroyer, however, progressively replaced the Marder II in infantry service during 1944, although a few Marder II vehicles continued to serve in German units until the very end of the war.

The high silhouette of the vehicle rendered the Marder II vulnerable to enemy fire. Nevertheless, the vehicle proved an effective and successful expedient that was quickly pushed into production.

BELOW *The tall gun cradle to support the long-barrelled main armament is prominent in this view of a 7.5cm-gunned Marder II (SdKfz 131). It was issued to Panzerjäger detachments, proving itself to be a capable weapons platform.*

PANZER 35(t)

The German Army's 1938 acquisition of Czech-built Panzer 35(t) tanks proved a useful boost to Germany's tank force during its early Blitzkrieg campaigns. By 1942, however, the tank had been outclassed and was withdrawn from frontline German service. It remained in service with the armies of Romania and Slovakia throughout the war.

On 15–16 March 1939, German forces occupied the rump state of Czechoslovakia, as it was constituted after the Munich Agreement of 30 September 1938. Hitler annexed the Protectorate of Bohemia-Moravia into the German Reich and Slovakia became a nominally autonomous Axis ally that, in reality, was nothing more than a puppet state. In the process of taking over the Czechoslovak state, the German Army gained access to the quality equipment of the Czechoslovak Army, previously considered one of the most effective armies in Europe. The Germans soon pressed into service the two principal Czech light/medium tanks – the LT35 and the LT38 – which they redesignated the Panzer 35(t) and 38(t),

LEFT A mixed battle group of Panzer 35(t) tanks with panzergrenadiers on foot or on motorcycles advance through open fields towards a wood. The tank crews have draped large Swastika flags over their vehicles' rear hulls as a recognition device for Luftwaffe aircraft.

respectively, the 't' suffix indicating the Czech origins of these tanks.

The LT35 first entered service as the main battle tank of the Czech Army in 1936. Initially, Czech tank crews were displeased with the vehicle because the early production machines possessed numerous mechanical defects that took more than a year to iron out totally. However, with these problems solved, the LT35 became a tank which was not only valued by the Czech Army itself, but one which sold well in the export market. Once it had been taken over by the German Army the LT35 was completely rebuilt to very advanced specifications – although many of the features proved to be highly complex and excess to requirements at that time.

Development History

The LT35/Panzer 35(t) was a 10.5-tonne (10.3-ton) light/medium tank, protected by bolted and riveted armour plates of 35mm- (1.4in-) thickness on the front and 16mm (0.6in) on the sides. The vehicle carried a 3.72cm Skoda A3 L/40 rifled gun, and two 7.92mm vz37 machine guns – one mounted co-axially in the turret and one in the hull front. When in Czech service the LT35 had a crew of three, though the Germans operated the Panzer 35(t) with a crew of four.

The Panzer 35(t) possessed a resilient suspension which was based on eight small, paired road wheels, suspended from two leaf springs. The combination of a strong suspension and a 120bhp Skoda T-11 petrol engine gave the tank a good maximum road speed of 40kph (25mph) and an effective road-based combat range of 200km (124 miles). The Panzer 35(t) also possessed a straightforward design that emphasised its ease of operation, in the form, for example, of pneumatic steering in order to alleviate driver fatigue. Rear sprockett drive and very wide tracks were also particular features of this tank. Unfortunately, while the vehicle was unquestionably easy to operate, it was also mechanically complex and the tank's German crews soon discovered that the Panzer 35(t) needed extensive maintenance if it was to remain fully operational.

A Stopgap Vehicle

Some 297 LT35 tanks were in service with the Czech Army in March 1939, and the German Army took more than 218 of them, while supplying the remaining 79 to Slovakia. The Germans allotted 112 of the redesignated Panzer 35(t) tanks to the 1st Light Division, a mechanised cavalry formation which was intended for reconnaissance and screening duties. The German Army used the Panzer 35(t) tank extensively in its invasion of Poland, as a stopgap vehicle until more Panzer III medium tanks could be rolled off the production lines.

Between the Polish and French Campaigns, the German-controlled Czech company of Skoda produced another 30 Panzer 35(t) tanks. Subsequently, this vehicle played a notable role in the German invasion of the West in May 1940, where the 6th Panzer Division – the upgraded 1st Light Division – fielded 116 Panzer 35(t) tanks. German forces guarding the new border between German-occupied Poland and the Soviet Union deployed a further 37 Panzer 35(t) tanks.

Germany also supplied some of its Axis allies with the 35(t), a total of 26 being supplied to the Army of Bulgaria in 1940, with another 10 being supplied direct from the manufacturer, Skoda, the same year. Skoda had also supplied Romania and Slovakia with large numbers of 35(t)s in 1939, and they saw service with these armies throughout the war.

On the eve of Operation 'Barbarossa', some 189 Panzer 35(t) tanks remained in German service, mainly attached to the 6th Panzer Division. This formation took an active part in the tremendous advances made by the German Army during Operation 'Barbarossa', before the momentum of this advance ground to a halt on the outskirts of Moscow itself amid the freezing winter conditions during December 1941.

By early 1942, the Panzer 35(t) had become increasingly obsolete but the Germans' desperate need for tanks made them reluctant to withdraw outclassed tanks until up-gunned Panzer III and Panzer IV tanks had arrived in larger numbers. Nonetheless, during the spring of 1942, the German Army subsequently withdrew from frontline service the few Panzer 35(t) tanks still deployed on the Eastern Front.

After the summer of 1942, the Panzer 35(t) only remained on active service with the armies of Germany's Axis Allies - particularly Slovakia and Rumania - on the Eastern Front. The élite Slovak Fast Division still fielded some LT35 and LT38 tanks during its retreat from the Caucasus in the winter of 1942/43, where its determined resistance earned the respect of the neighbouring German units. A regiment of Czech LT35 tanks, purchased by Romania before the war, also served in the Romanian 1st Armoured Division until November 1942 when the Soviet counter-offensive that encircled the Sixth German Army at Stalingrad destroyed the regiment.

The German Army had already decided back in early 1940 that the 35(t) chassis was not suitable as the basis for a self-propelled gun, and so it took the unusual decision to terminate production of the 35(t) chassis in the summer of 1940, at the same time as it ceased construction of the tank itself. From 1942, the Germans converted many of the few Panzer 35(t) tanks which were still operational, into tractors for the transportation of mortar and artillery shells. The conversion process involved removing the turrets to create a two-man carrier capable of pulling loads of up to 12 tonnes (11.8 tons). A similar conversion produced a towing vehicle used in the recovery of disabled tanks. These conversions reflected the new German High Command policy, adopted in 1942, that panzer units were to undertake every effort to recover damaged tanks before they fell into enemy hands.

Panzer 35(t) in Poland

A total of 298 Panzer 35(t) tanks served with the Axis armed forces that invaded Poland. The majority – some 218 tanks – served with the German Army, while the remaining 79 LT35 vehicles fought with the Slovakian Army's Fast Division. Of those vehicles in German service, 112 tanks fought with the 1st Light Division, one of four such divisions designed as light-armour versions of the panzer divisions. The light divisions had much less armour than their panzer-formation counterparts, although the 1st Light was the most powerful of the light divisions. For in addition to more than 100 Panzer I and II tanks and a handful of Panzer III and IV vehicles common to all the light divisions, the Germans augmented the 1st Light Division with four extra medium companies, equipped with Panzer 35(t) tanks.

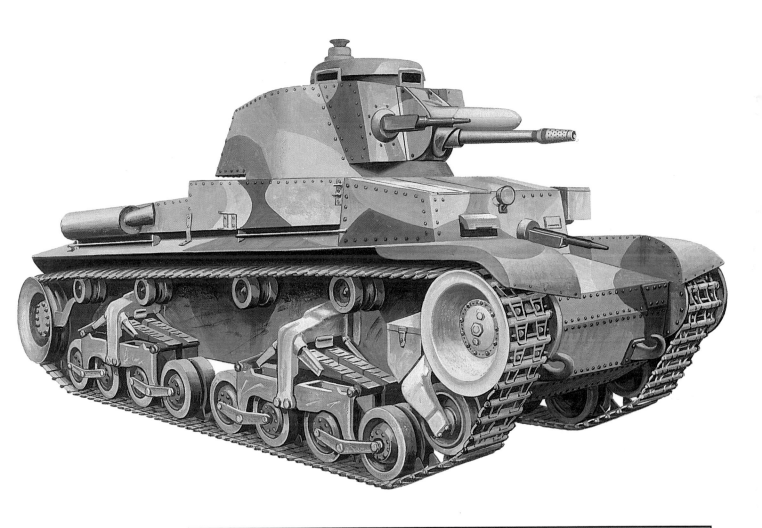

SPECIFICATIONS: Panzer 35(t)

GENERAL
Vehicle Type: light/medium tank
Entered Service: 1935 (Czech Army); spring 1939 (German Army)
Crew: four
Combat Weight: 10.5 tonnes (10.3 tons)

DIMENSIONS
Overall Length: 4.45m (14ft 7in)
Hull Length: 4.45m (14ft 7in)
Width: 2.14m (7ft)
Height: 2.20m (7ft 3in)

ARMAMENT
Main: 3.72cm (1.5in) KwK A3(t) L/40

Secondary: 2 x 7.92mm (0.312in) MG(t); 1 coaxial in turret; 1 hull front

AMMUNITION STOWAGE
Main: 72 rounds
Secondary: 1800 rounds

ARMOUR
Hull Front (Nose): 25mm (1in) (at 40 degrees)
Hull Front (Driver's Plate): 25mm (1in) (at 76 degrees)
Hull Sides: 16mm (0.6in) (at 87 degrees)
Hull Rear: 16mm (0.6in) (at 30 degrees)
Turret Front: 25mm (1in) (at 85 degrees)
Turret Sides: 15mm (0.6in) (at 76 degrees)

Turret Rear: 15mm (0.6in) (at 82 degrees)
Turret Roof: 12mm (0.5in) (at 0–5 degrees)

MOTIVE POWER
Engine: Skoda T11 R4-cylinder petrol
Power: 120 bhp
Fuel capacity: 153 litres (34 gallons)

PERFORMANCE
Maximum Road Speed: 40kph (25mph)
Maximum Cross-Country Speed: 20kph (12.5mph)
Operational Range (Road): 190km (118 miles)
Operational Range (Cross-Country): 115km (71.5 miles)

ABOVE *A column of Czech-designed tanks belonging to Germany's Slovakian Axis ally in the opening months of Operation 'Barbarossa'. The tank in the foreground and the one in the left background are Panzer 38(t) vehicles, the other three are Panzer 35(t) tanks.*

The German Army used Panzer 35(t) tanks in Poland to augment its medium tank complements. However, delays in the production of the Panzer III medium and Panzer IV medium/heavy tanks meant that Germany's panzer forces were forced to rely very heavily on the ineffectual Panzer I and II light tanks in combat in Poland. Under these circumstances, the German Army's acquisition of the 3.7cm gunned Panzer 35(t) tanks was a very welcome addition to the striking power of Germany's armoured forces.

The Panzer 35(t) tank played a significant part in the Polish Campaign. On 3 September 1939, the third day of the Campaign, the 1st Light Division fought a fierce engagement to establish a bridgehead over the River Warta. The 3.7cm guns of the Panzer 35(t) provided intense fire support from the rear, which helped the German assault infantry get across the river and establish a toe-hold on the marshy ground on the opposite bank. In subsequent rapid

advances toward the River Vistula and beyond, the Panzer 35(t) showed its tactical worth and the tank's 3.7cm gun proved effective against the lightly armoured Polish TK and TKS tankettes.

During the eight-day, 800km (497 mile) advance of the 1st Light Division toward Radom, the Panzer 35(t) also proved its general mechanical reliability and mobility, although its heavy maintenance requirements also became evident. Problems of mechanical reliability had dogged the peaceful German panzer advance into Austria in 1938, and the Germans were grateful that for the Polish Campaign they could field a newly acquired tank that proved reliable. The heavy casualties suffered by armoured units equipped with the Panzer 35(t) in Poland indicates that the vehicle played a prominent role in the battles fought by the 1st Light in its rapid advance: of its 112 Panzer 35(t) tanks, no fewer than 12 were destroyed and another 65 damaged during the campaign.

Panzer 35(t) in Russia

In June 1941, a total of 189 Panzer 35(t) tanks took part in the German invasion of the Soviet Union. The majority of these tanks served with the 6th Panzer Division, which the Germans had raised in 1940 by upgrading the 1st Light Division. Unfortunately, this formation lost many of its Panzer 35(t) tanks during the bitter battles fought during the opening months of Operation 'Barbarossa', particularly in the early December 1941 engagements around Klin, close to Moscow.

The Germans discovered during the bitterly cold Russian winter of 1941–42, however, that the pneumatic steering system fitted to the Panzer 35(t) froze easily. As a result, German units had to fit special heating units to prevent the steering system freezing solid. Moreover, given the lack of anti-freeze, German crews often had to light fires under their tanks and start their engines every 30 minutes to stop them freezing. Also, the 35(t) lacked the useful emergency manual engine-starter fitted to the Panzer I-IV and the 38(t). Partly because these problems, the Germans sent back the remnants of the Panzer 35(t)-equipped 6th Division to Germany during early 1942 for re-equipment with modern Panzer III tanks.

Withdrawal from Frontline Service

Not every Panzer 35(t) in German Army possession on the eve of Operation 'Barbarossa', however, fought in the campaign. The High Command held back a small number of 35(t) tanks in the Reich as a reserve. In September 1941, the German Army used these vehicles to fit out the newly raised 22nd Panzer Division. The Germans then redeployed this formation to the Eastern Front in the spring of 1942, and thus the Panzer 35(t) made its second appearance on the Eastern Front. Subsequently, the Czech tanks of the 22nd Panzer Division took part in the ambitious German summer 1942 drive toward the oil-rich Caucasus and the city of Stalingrad. The mighty Soviet counter-offensive in the winter of 1942–43 shattered the 22nd Panzer Division and it lost all of its few remaining Panzer 35(t) vehicles.

After these events the Panzer 35(t) tank disappeared from frontline service on the Eastern Front, although the Germans retained some for anti-partisan duties in rear areas. A few Panzer 35(t) tanks even fired their guns in combat as late as 1944, although this time it was against the German Army! For a few of the LT35 tanks still left in the Slovak Army participated in the Slovakian national uprising against the Nazis of August 1944. Every one of these LT35 tanks, however, speedily succumbed to the vastly superior firepower deployed by the Germans to suppress the uprising.

BELOW *The riveted armour so characteristic of Czech-designed tanks is clearly visible on this Panzer 35(t), as is the distinctive tracking which sloped downwards towards the rear idler wheel. Note also the unusual design of the tank's main armament, the 3.72cm Skoda A3 gun.*

CHAPTER 6

PANZER 38(t)

During 1939–41, the German Army relied heavily on the reliable Czech-designed Panzer 38(t) tank to supplement its modest number of Panzer III medium tanks. The Ausf D, E and F models served with the German Panzer divisions in Russia from the start of Operation 'Barbarossa' in July 1941, and the Ausf G version was still in reserve service in late 1944.

When Nazi Germany occupied Czechoslovakia on 15–16 March 1939, the TNHP-S or LT38 light tank was the Czechoslovakian Army's latest armoured fighting vehicle. Production of the LT38 had only commenced in late 1938 and by mid-March 1939, only a single vehicle from the initial production batch had actually been completed, though eight more vehicles were in advanced stages of construction. During May 1939, the German Army conducted extensive tests on the LT38 which revealed the tank to be an excellent vehicle, superior in performance to the Panzer I and II and equal to that of the Panzer III. By this date, Czech armament factories, now under German control, had completed the initial batch of

nine LT38 tanks, which the German Army took over and redesignated as the Panzer 38(t).

In late May 1939, the German Weapons Department issued contracts to the original producers of the LT38, CKD of Prague, now renamed Bohemia-Moravia Machine Works (BMM), to construct the 150 vehicles already on the firm's order books from the original 1938 Czech contract. The company produced these 150 vehicles, designated the Panzer 38(t) Model A, between May and November 1939 at an average rate of 21 units per month. Later in 1939, the Germans asked BMM to build a further 325 slightly modified Panzer 38(t) Model B, C and D vehicles. The firm completed this order over an 11-month period, beginning in January 1940, at an average rate of 30 tanks per month. The Germans subsequently issued additional orders for another 525 Panzer 38(t) Model E and F tanks. The Prague-based firm completed this order in a year-long production run that lasted from November 1940 to October 1941, delivering the

LEFT *A group of Panzer 38(t) tanks of the 25th Panzer Regiment of General Rommel's 7th Panzer Division take a well-earned rest. Shortly after, they were thrown into an assault on the French defensive positions along the Somme river.*

vehicles at an average rate of 44 machines per month. Finally, BMM delivered 321 Panzer 38(t) Model G tanks, the final production version, from a contract for 500 machines, between October 1941 and July 1942, when all Panzer 38(t) tank production ceased. Between 1939 and 1942 BMM constructed about five percent of the Panzer 38 (t) Model A-G vehicles it produced as command tanks, for a total of about 70 machines.

The only other tank project connected to the Panzer 38(t) was the TNHnA or Panzer 38(t)nA (nA meaning 'new design') fast-reconnaissance tank. This had 35mm- (1.4in-) thick welded armour that took the vehicle's weight up to 15 tonnes (14.7 tons), but this was more than compensated for by the installation of a much more powerful 250bhp Praga V8-cylinder engine, which produced an impressive top road speed of 60kph (37mph). In German Army trials undertaken in 1942, however, the 38(t)nA lost out to rival fast tank designs and the Germans cancelled the project after BMM had produced just 15 pre-production vehicles.

The Panzer 38(t) was an excellent light/medium tank that balanced nicely the requirements of firepower, protection and mobility. Its main armament consisted of a 3.72cm Skoda A7 L/40 gun, although some vehicles constructed under German auspices mounted the German 3.7cm KwK L/45. The A7 Skoda gun possessed greater penetration than the 3.72cm A3 gun fitted to the Panzer 35(t). The armour-piercing round that the A7 gun fired could penetrate 32mm (1.3in) of armour at 1100m

(3608ft). The vehicle carried 90 rounds for its main armament, most of which were stored in the large bin located at the rear of the turret.

The armour protection of the Panzer 38(t) Model A ranged from a maximum thickness of 25mm (1in) of riveted steel on the hull front to only 8mm (0.3in) on the hull top. German tank factories added an additional 25mm (1in) armour plate to the hull front from the Model E onwards, increasing frontal protection to 50mm (2in). Early German-produced 38(t) tanks continued to use the original Praga 125bhp engine, although the last 500 tanks that BMM delivered carried a more powerful 150bhp EPA/AAC engine. This engine gave the Panzer 38(t) a respectable maximum road speed of 42kph (26mph) and an impressive operational range of 250km (155 miles).

The Germans found their acquisition of the reliable and robust Panzer 38(t), and its subsequent production under German control, a useful interim measure to plug the gap caused by slower than anticipated delivery of Panzer III and IV tanks. Between 1939 and 1942, when it became obsolete as a frontline battle tank, the Panzer 38(t) proved a highly effective light/medium tank in German service. The Germans used the vehicle within their panzer divisions both to support the Panzer III medium tank and to supplement the Panzer I and II light tanks in a reconnaissance role.

BMM produced the Panzer 38(t) tank over a period of three years and three months between May 1939 and July 1942. In total the firm delivered 1414 Panzer 38(t) tanks, at an average rate of 36 vehicles per month. Production rates peaked during 1941, when BMM constructed 698 vehicles

at an average rate of 58 machines per month. Of this total production run, the Germans supplied 231 Panzer 38(t) tanks to their Axis allies to bolster their meagre armoured forces.

Specialised Variants

By mid-1942, the Panzer 38(t) was approaching obsolescence as a frontline combat tank and so German

SPECIFICATIONS: Panzer 38(t) Model A

GENERAL
Vehicle Type: light/medium tank
Entered Service: 1938 (Czech Army), spring 1939 (German Army)
Crew: four
Combat Weight: 9.7 tonnes (9.5 tons)

DIMENSIONS
Overall Length: 4.90m (16ft 1in)
Hull Length: 4.90m (16ft 1in)
Width: 2.06m (6ft 9in)
Height: 2.37m (7ft 9in)

ARMAMENT
Main: 3.7cm (1.5in) KwK A7(t) L/40; or 37mm (1.46in) KwK L/45.
Secondary: 2 x 7.92mm (0.312in) MG

37(t); 1 coaxial in turret; 1 hull front.

AMMUNITION STOWAGE
Main: 90 rounds
Secondary: 2700 rounds

ARMOUR
Hull Front (Nose): 25mm (1in) (at 25 degrees)
Hull Front (Driver's Plate): 25mm (1in) (at 80 degrees)
Hull Sides: 17.5mm (0.7in) (at 90 degrees)
Hull Rear: 10mm (0.4in) (at 80 degrees)
Turret Front: 25mm (1in) (at 84 degrees)
Turret Sides: 25mm (1in) (at 74 degrees)
Turret Rear: 25mm (1in) (at 86 degrees)

Turret Roof: 10mm (0.4in) (at 0–4 degrees)

MOTIVE POWER
Engine: (Czech) Praga EPA TZJ R6-cylinder petrol
Power: 125 bhp
Fuel Capacity: 218 litres (48 gallons)

PERFORMANCE
Maximum Road Speed: 42kph (26mph)
Maximum Cross-Country Speed: 15kph (9mph)
Operational Range (Road): 230km (143 miles)
Operational Range (Cross-Country): 165km (103 miles)

factories converted many of them into self-propelled anti-tank guns. During 1942–43, the Germans converted 175 Panzer 38(t) tanks into self-propelled guns carriages that mounted the 7.5cm Pak 40/3 anti-tank gun. Another 19 Panzer 38(t) tanks were converted into Marder III tank-destroyers that carried the captured Soviet 7.62cm Pak 36(r) anti-tank gun. During 1943–44, some 70 Panzer 38(t) reconnaissance tanks were produced by removing the original tank turret and replacing it with an armoured car turret. These vehicles were issued to armoured reconnaissance battalions of élite panzer divisions. Additional vehicles had their turrets removed for use as munitions tractors.

Even though the German Army ceased Panzer 38(t) tank production in July 1942, German armaments firms continued to construct the excellent 38(t) chassis at an ever-increasing rate until March 1945. In fact, after October 1944 the basis of all German armoured fighting vehicle construction was rationalised to just three chassis: the 38(t), the Panther and the King Tiger. Between 1942 and 1944, some 344 newly built 38(t) chassis were used as platforms for Marder III self-propelled guns. Another 2396 extended 38(t) chassis were produced during 1944–45 as the basis of the Jagdpanzer 38(t) Hetzer (Baiter) light tank-destroyer, while another 162 chassis were utilised as the basis of the Flakpanzer 38(t). This was an interim anti-aircraft tank that mounted a single 2cm anti-aircraft cannon,

designed to counter the growing Allied air menace until the purpose-built Flakpanzer IV anti-aircraft tank could enter German service. Lastly, during 1944 some 102 improved 38(t) Model K chassis were produced as munitions carriers.

In total, the Germans produced some 4600 additional 38(t) chassis as the basis for self-propelled anti-tank guns, Hetzer tank-destroyers, and sundry other specialised armoured fighting vehicles. When added to the 1414 Panzer 38(t) and 15 Panzer 38(t)nA tanks that Germany produced, BMM manufactured more than 6000 Panzer 38(t) chassis during the course of the war, a testament to the dependability and ruggedness of the original Czech design.

Panzer 38(t) in Combat

For the Axis invasion of Poland, the Germans deployed 80 Panzer 38(t) Model A tanks with the 2nd and 3rd Light Divisions. These formations were smaller and less powerful versions of a full panzer division, intended for reconnaissance and screening duties. After the German triumph in Poland, both these divisions were upgraded to full panzer status as the 7th and 8th Panzer Divisions. During April 1940, some 15 Panzer 38(t) tanks also participated in the German invasion of Norway.

Quickening German production of the Panzer 38(t) Model B in early 1940 boosted the numbers available to Germany's panzer forces. Consequently, by the time of the May 1940 German campaign in the West, the Panzer 38(t) constituted nearly one-tenth of the German tank strength. The Germans employed in the West 228 of the 238 Panzer 38(t) tanks then available, out of an overall invasion force of 2574 tanks. Most of the Panzer 38(t) tanks were again concentrated in the 7th and 8th Panzer Divisions, where

BELOW *A picture purportedly taken by Rommel from his divisional command vehicle showing Panzer 38(t) tanks of his 7th Panzer Division in France during May 1940. The closest tank, vehicle RØ1, is the command variant belonging to the commander of the division's panzer regiment.*

they were substituted for missing Panzer III tanks in medium tank companies. General Erwin Rommel's famous 7th Panzer Division – soon to be nicknamed the 'Ghost' division for the speed of its advance – deployed 132 Panzer 38(t) tanks, while the 8th Panzer Division fielded 85 Panzer 38(t) tanks.

Rommel's 7th Panzer Division was part of General Hoth's XV Panzer Corps which achieved strategic surprise by infiltrating through the northern Ardennes in accordance with Erich von Manstein's cunning Sichelschnitt (Cut of the Scythe) plan. At first light on 15 May 1940, Rommel's Division burst out of its bridgehead over the River Meuse; but then for the first time, it encountered the French heavy Char B tank near Flavion, which proved more than a match for any German tank then in service. Rommel's Division engaged elements of the 1st French Armoured Division which fielded 68 Char B tanks as well as 90 lighter Hotchkiss H35 tanks. The Germans discovered to their dismay that the 3.7cm gun of the Panzer 38(t) could not penetrate the 60mm (2.4in) frontal armour of the Char B. The German Panzer 38(t) tank crews, however, soon learned to aim for vulnerable spots on the enemy tank, such as the radiator louvres and the tracks, in order to disable the massive French vehicles. This minor tactical setback did not deter Rommel, the dashing armoured commander: he by-passed the French resistance and allowed follow-up armoured forces and German air power to mop up the French tanks. In the meantime, Rommel continued his devastating whirlwind dash towards the Channel in a

ABOVE *The last battle of the Panzer 38(t). Despite being withdrawn from German service, this Czech tank continued to see action in the East with the Romanian Army. This column is defending the Axis bridgehead at Kuban – its toe-hold beyond the Kerch peninsula in the northern Caucasus region.*

textbook implementation of the German Blitzkrieg style of armoured warfare.

By the start of Operation 'Barbarossa', the number of Panzer 38(t) tanks available had risen to 754. During the first weeks of the invasion, the Panzer 38(t) accounted for nearly one-quarter of the German tanks engaged, with most vehicles being concentrated in five panzer divisions – the 7th, 8th, 12th, 19th and 20th. Despite increased production, the heavy losses incurred in 'Barbarossa' ensured that the number of Panzer 38(t) tanks in service on the Eastern Front fell to 522 by April 1942. The experience of fighting the new Soviet T34 and KV1 tanks also highlighted the growing ineffectiveness of the Panzer 38(t). Yet the need to keep up the numbers in the field prompted the Germans to continue producing this reliable tank until July 1942. Increasingly, from the summer of 1942, as the Panzer 38(t) became obsolete, the Germans either transferred remaining vehicles to non-combat duties or converted them into self-propelled anti-tank guns and other specialised armoured fighting vehicles. A few Panzer 38(t) tanks, however, remained in frontline service on the Eastern Front with the army of Germany's Romanian Axis partner. Some 229 Panzer 38(t) tanks remained in German service on occupation duties throughout Nazi-controlled Europe as late as mid-1944.

CHAPTER 7

MARDER III

Operation 'Barbarossa', the German invasion of the Soviet Union in the summer of 1941, exposed the consequences of Germany's neglect of mobile anti-tank vehicles. To redress this failure the German Army improvised the Marder III self-propelled gun that married potent anti-tank guns to the reliable 38(t) tank chassis.

Although by the outbreak of World War II, Germany had created a powerful tank force capable of independent strategic operations, the offensively oriented German Army had devoted little energy to stopping enemy tanks. When Germany invaded the Soviet Union, her forces soon found that the standard German towed 3.7cm, 4.7cm and 5cm anti-tank guns proved ineffective against the frontal armour of the new Soviet T34 medium and KV1 heavy tanks. Moreover, as the Germans plunged ever deeper into the Soviet Union, their forces became more thinly stretched and hence increasingly vulnerable to Soviet counter-thrusts. Thereafter, autumn mud and winter snow exacerbated mounting equipment

LEFT *A knocked out 7.5cm-gunned Marder III Model M (Sdkfz 138) self-propelled anti-tank gun. This particular variant had its engine located well forward and the superstructure fitted towards the rear of the vehicle.*

shortages and left German infantry dangerously exposed to armoured counter-attacks. German troops across the front clamoured for greater and more mobile anti-tank firepower. The German Army's entire inventory of Panzerjäger (self-propelled anti-tank guns) at the start of 'Barbarossa', however, consisted of a mere 132 Panzerjäger I vehicles that mounted a Czech 4.7cm anti-tank gun in an open and vulnerable fighting compartment on top of the chassis of the Panzer I tank.

Development History

In response to these Eastern Front experiences, on 22 December 1941 the Army Weapons Department ordered the design and construction of an improvised, lightly armoured tank destroyer. This vehicle, designated the Marder III, mounted the captured Soviet 7.62cm M36 field gun (rechambered to take the standard German 7.5cm anti-tank round) on the reliable Panzer 38(t) tank chassis. German

LEFT *A 7.5cm-gunned Marder III with its forward sited superstructures, in combat on the Eastern Front. The rear-mounted engine and forward-place fighting compartment made it both front- and top-heavy.*

factories designed a new superstructure to incorporate the Soviet gun and its entire carriage, which was fixed on top of the Panzer 38(t) Model G chassis, via a specially designed turntable plate. This superstructure comprised a small, three-sided, thinly armoured shell of 10mm- (0.4in-) thick plate with an elongated gun shield and fixed sides that provided the gunner and loader with rudimentary protection against small-arms fire. This fighting compartment was bolted onto the gun shield and affixed to the mounting by tubular supports, so that the entire armoured shield traversed with the gun. A sliding mantlet was also set in the shield to permit elevation and depression of the gun. The lower, and larger, section of the fighting compartment was bolted to the superstructure and consisted of 15mm- (0.6in-) thick plate.

The 4.2m- (13ft 9in-) long Soviet 7.62cm gun mounted in the Marder III was located well forward and hence projected well beyond the front of the vehicle. This gun possessed a muzzle velocity of 551 metres per second (1805 feet per second) firing high-explosive shells and 990m/s (3249 f/s) when firing armour-piercing rounds. The latter shell could penetrate an impressive 81mm- (3.2in-) thickness of 30-degree sloped armour at 914m (9228ft). For local defence purposes, the vehicle retained the standard secondary armament of the Panzer 38(t) tank, a 7.92mm MG 37(t) machine gun mounted in the hull front, as well as a smoke discharger.

The Germans kept the modifications to the basic chassis to a minimum in order to speed production. As a consequence the vehicle possessed a relatively high silhouette for its size, standing 2.5m (8ft 2in) tall. The mechanical layout and components of the vehicle were identical to those of the Panzer 38(t) Model G and the conversion was achieved by removing the turret and hull

top-plate of the original tank. The addition of a 76.2mm gun that was far larger than the 37.2mm one originally carried by the Panzer 38(t) tank, however, appreciably increased the weight of the vehicle to 10.7 tonnes (10.5 tons). To keep down the vehicle's weight on a chassis that was already close to being overloaded, the fighting compartment could only be lightly armoured and had to be left open-topped. Hence the crew remained vulnerable to enemy fire, especially shrapnel. The larger gun also left the small chassis cramped and overcrowded. Consequently, available ammunition storage was a meagre 36 rounds, which restricted the tactical employment of the vehicle. Moreover, space limitations necessitated storing rounds on the thinly armoured superstructure walls, a dangerous practice given the vehicle's limited protection.

The 7.62cm-gunned Marder III

The German Army officially designated this vehicle the Panzerjäger 38(t) für 7.62cm Pak 36(r) (Sdkfz 139), with Hitler personally bestowing the vehicle with the name Marder (Marten) III on 27 February 1942. Production began on 24 March 1942 at BMM in Prague, with 17 Marder III vehicles constructed in the first month against an initial target goal of 30 units per month. The first vehicles reached German infantry on the Eastern Front in April 1942, where they quickly proved their tactical worth as the only available mobile anti-tank weapons capable of destroying the Soviet T34 tank at typical combat ranges. Hitler, however, ordered most of the initial batch of vehicles dispatched to North Africa to combat the formidable British Matilda II heavy tank, the frontal armour of which was invulnerable to the German 5cm anti-tank gun except at point-blank range. So impressed with the Marder III were Commonwealth troops that they thought that they were facing mobile 8.8cm guns!

The 7.5cm-gunned Marder III

The new 7.5cm-gunned Marder III (Sdkfz 138) vehicle dispensed with the lower-hull shielding present on its predecessor and instead mounted a larger shield (to encompass the bigger German gun) directly on the chassis, giving the vehicle a lower silhouette. The shield remained, however, open to the rear and top due to weight restrictions. In addition, the vehicle carried a gun rest mounted on the front hull to limit wear and tear on the overhanging barrel while travelling long distances. German factories produced 418 7.5cm-gunned Marder III (Sdkfz 138) vehicles during 1942–43, of which 175 were direct conversions from obsolete Panzer 38(t) tanks rather than vehicles constructed on newly produced 38(t) chassis. During 1942–44, these 75mm-gunned Marder III (Sdkfz 138) vehicles saw service on the Eastern Front, in Tunisia, and in Italy with infantry division anti-tank battalions and independent army anti-tank units.

In total, German factories constructed 975 Marder III (Sdkfz 138) Model M vehicles. After mid-1942, when production of the Panzer 38(t) tank stopped, the 38(t) chassis continued to be produced primarily as the platform for the 7.5cm-gunned Marder III.

Although an improvised solution, the Marder III was an effective vehicle that quickly married two powerful anti-tank guns with a readily available platform to provide German infantry with a mobile anti-tank capability.

SPECIFICATIONS: Panzerjäger Marder III Model M (Sdkfz 138)

GENERAL
Vehicle Type: light tank destroyer (self-propelled anti-tank gun)
Entered Service: summer 1943
Crew: four
Combat Weight: 10.5 tonnes (10.3 tons)
Chassis: Panzer 38(t)

DIMENSIONS
Overall Length: 4.65m (15ft 3in)
Hull Length: 4.65m (15ft 3in)
Width: 2.16m (7ft 1in)
Height: 2.48m (7ft 10in)

ARMAMENT
Main: 7.5cm (3in) Pak 40/3 L/46 gun
Main Gun Traverse: 30 degrees left to 30 degrees right

Secondary: none

AMMUNITION STOWAGE
Main: 38 rounds
Secondary: none

ARMOUR
Hull Front (Nose): 20mm (0.8in) (at 80 degrees)
Hull Front (Driver's Plate): 25mm (1in) (at 78 degrees)
Hull Sides: 15mm (0.6in) (at 90 degrees)
Hull Rear: 8mm (0.3in) (at 90 degrees)
Superstructure Front: 25mm (1in) (at 74 degrees)
Superstructure Sides: 10mm (0.4in) (at 78 degrees)

Superstructure Rear: none
Superstructure Roof: none

MOTIVE POWER
Engine: (Czech) Praga EPA TZJ R6-cylinder petrol
Power: 125 bhp
Fuel Capacity: 218 litres (48 gallons)

PERFORMANCE
Maximum Speed (Road): 42kph (26mph)
Maximum Speed (Cross-Country): 24kph (15mph)
Operational Range (Road): 185km (115 miles)
Operational Range (Cross-Country): 140km (87 miles)

CHAPTER 8

PANZER III

Germany's first significant combat tank, the Panzer III became the backbone of the German armoured force during the mighty 1941 Nazi onslaught against the Red Army. Outclassed by the latest Soviet armour, the Germans eventually began phasing out the Panzer III from frontline service in late 1943. Small numbers, however, continued in German service until the end of the war.

The Panzer III (Sdkfz 141) medium tank was the first major combat tank project undertaken by Nazi Germany after its renunciation of the Treaty of Versailles in 1933. The Panzer I and II light tanks were designed merely as stop-gap machines that would suffice until the late 1930s, when the Panzer III medium and Panzer IV medium/heavy tanks came on stream as the core of the German Army's panzer force.

In 1935, the German Army Weapons Department issued orders for German armaments firms to develop a medium tank in the 15-tonne (14.8-ton) class. To keep secret from its enemies the fact that it was developing a medium tank, the German Army designated the project under the pseudonym

LEFT An early 3.7cm gunned Panzer III Model F advances through a burning landscape during the stunning early successes of Operation 'Barbarossa', the summer 1941 German invasion of the Soviet Union. Note the stowage box retro-fitted to the rear of the tank's turret.

ZW – for Zugführerwagen or troop commander's vehicle – which implied that the project involved an unarmoured tracked vehicle. In late 1936, extensive trials at the Kummersdorf and Ulm proving grounds in Germany tested four prototypes, produced by the firms of MAN in Nuremberg, Krupp in Essen as well as Daimler-Benz and Rheinmetall-Borsig, both in Berlin. As a result of these thorough trials, the Weapons Department placed an initial order with Daimler-Benz.

Development History

The first 10 pre-production 1/ZW vehicles (later to be redesignated the Panzer III Model A) were completed in 1936. The German Army viewed these tanks as the first in a series of developmental vehicles to test various suspension arrangements. The Panzer III Model A tank had a crew of five, weighed 15 tonnes (14.8 tons), and had 15mm- (0.6in-) thick armour on the front and sides. The tank's

LEFT *Tank crews relax with a game of cards and some musical accompaniment in a rare quiet period during the German invasion of the Balkans. Behind them is a Panzer III Model F that has been up-gunned with the more potent 5cm L/42 weapon.*

rounds. The German Army tested these 10 vehicles on active service during the Polish Campaign but withdrew them in February 1940 before the German invasion of the West.

The second model, the 2/ZW or Panzer III Model B, appeared in 1937 at which time 15 examples were produced. The Model B was very similar to the Model A, except that its suspension had been redesigned by Daimler-Benz. The new arrangement featured eight small bogie wheels per side, grouped in pairs and suspended on just two semi-elliptical springs, together with three return rollers, instead of the two in the previous variant. The Model B carried fewer main armament rounds – 121 instead of 150 – to offset the extra weight of the new suspension. Despite these modifications, the tank's performance was virtually identical to that of its predecessor. These 15 Panzer III Model B vehicles also served in the Polish Campaign, but the German Army withdrew them from frontline service before its invasion of France.

Between early 1937 and January 1938, Daimler-Benz produced 15 3/ZW or Panzer III Model C vehicles. These tanks featured another redesigned suspension, based on eight bogie wheels as in the previous variant, but this time suspended from three, rather than two, semi-elliptic

suspension consisted of five independently sprung medium-sized bogie wheels with two return rollers. The Model A was powered by a 230bhp Maybach HL 108 TR petrol engine that enabled the vehicle to achieve a top speed of 32kph (20mph) and an effective operational range of 165km (103 miles). The tank mounted the 3.7cm KwK L/45 gun as its main armament and carried 150 rounds for this weapon. The tank also mounted three 7.92mm MG 34 machine-guns – two coaxially in the turret plus a third in the hull front-plate – for which the vehicle carried 4500

leaf springs. The weight of this vehicle rose to 16 tonnes (15.7 tons), an increase which resulted in the tank's effective range dropping to 105km (65 miles). This variant, like both of its predecessors, also served in the Polish Campaign.

The fourth variant, the Panzer III Model D, incorporated heavier armour of up to 30mm (1.2in) thickness that markedly increased the vehicle's weight to 19.3 tonnes (19 tons). The vehicle featured yet more modifications to the suspension, and although it carried the same amount of fuel as its predecessors, it did so in four fuel tanks instead of two. German factories produced a total of 40 Model D tanks between January and June 1938, and these saw active service both during the German invasion of Poland and the occupation of Norway.

Daimler-Benz produced the last pre-production variant, the Model E, between December 1938 and October 1939. This vehicle was the first of the experimental models to go into sustained production, with 96 vehicles being delivered to the German Army. The Model E incorporated major modifications including a more powerful 320bhp Maybach HL 120 TR engine and a new transmission. The tank also featured yet another redesigned suspension based on six independent bogie road wheels, suspended from transverse torsion bars. The majority of the 98 Panzer III tanks deployed by the Germans during the Polish Campaign were Model E vehicles. This tank also took part in active operations in the West in 1940, the Soviet Union in 1941–42 and in North Africa up to late 1942.

General Production Models

The first general production model was the Model F, which entered service from late 1939. German tank factories delivered 435 Model F tanks in an 11-month production run between September 1939 and July 1940. The high standard of mechanical reliability evident in the Model F was the product of the experimentation undertaken with the previous five pre-production designs. The German combat experiences in Poland and France, however, had convinced

BELOW *A column of Panzer III tanks advances through a Soviet village past Red Army prisoners during the early stages of Operation 'Barbarossa'. The nearest tank carries an additional stowage box on the rear of the hull decking, presumably rescued from a destroyed Panzer III tank.*

the Army Weapons Department that the Panzer III needed to mount a more powerful main armament than the existing 3.7cm gun. Yet the High Command recognised that it would take many months to develop and install such a weapon in the Panzer III and it decided to continue to produce Model F tanks with the existing 3.7cm gun, so as not to delay the entry of these vehicles into German service.

From mid-1940 onwards, the various new Panzer III models that appeared all reflected the growing tactical requirements for increased firepower and enhanced armour protection. Entering service in April 1940, the Model G mounted (with the exception of the very earliest vehicles) the more powerful 5cm KwK L/42 gun. During the winter of 1940–41, in addition to the completion of Model G tanks, German factories retro-fitted many existing Panzer III Model

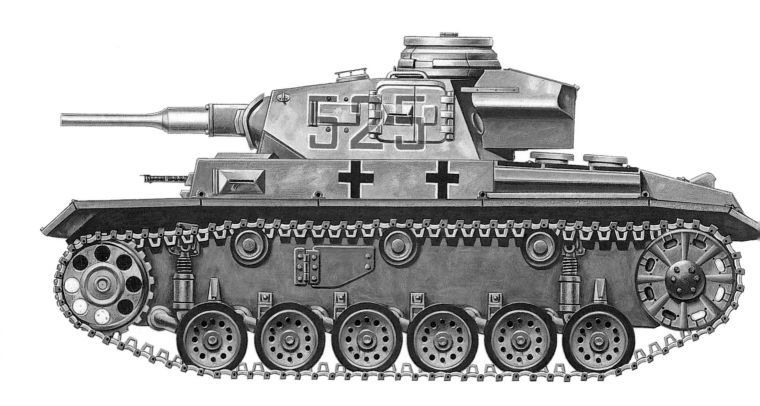

SPECIFICATIONS: Panzer III Model A (Sdkfz 141)

GENERAL
Vehicle Type: medium tank
Entered Service: late 1936
Crew: five
Combat Weight: 15 tonnes
(14.8 tons)

DIMENSIONS
Overall Length: 5.69m (18ft 8in)
Hull Length: 5.69m (18ft 8in)
Width: 2.81m (9ft 3in)
Height: 2.34m (7ft 8in)

ARMAMENT
Main: 3.7cm (1.5in) KwK L/45 gun
Secondary: 3 x 7.92mm (0.312in)
MG 34; 2 coaxial in turret;
1 hull front.

AMMUNITION STOWAGE
Main: 150 rounds
Secondary: 4500 rounds

ARMOUR
Hull Front (Nose): 14.5mm (0.6in)
(at 69 degrees)
Hull Front (Driver's Plate): 14.5mm
(0.6in) (at 81 degrees)
Hull Sides: 14.5mm (0.6in) (at 90 degrees)
Hull Rear: 14.5mm (0.6in)
(at 77–80 degrees)
Turret Front: 14.5mm (0.6in)
(at 75 degrees)
Turret Sides: 14.5mm (0.6in)
(at 65 degrees)
Turret Rear: 14.5mm (0.6in)
(at 78 degrees)

Turret Roof: 10mm (0.4in)
(at 0–7 degrees)

MOTIVE POWER
Engine: Maybach HL 108 TR V12-cylinder petrol
Power: 230 bhp
Fuel Capacity: 300 litres (66 gallons)

PERFORMANCE
Maximum Road Speed: 32kph
(20mph)
Maximum Cross-Country Speed:
19kph (12mph)
Operational Range (Road): 150km
(93 miles)
Operational Range (Cross-Country):
95km (59 miles)

A–F tanks with the more powerful 5cm L/42 weapon. In
total, some 450 Model G tanks were produced between
April 1940 and February 1941.

German factories constructed a further 310 tanks of an
eighth Panzer III variant – the Model H – between October
1940 and April 1941. On the basis of combat experiences
gained in France, the German Army had also recognised that
the Panzer III was insufficiently armoured. As a contingency
measure to correct this deficiency, German factories bolted
additional 30mm (1.2in) appliqué plates onto the existing
30mm- (1.2in-) thick frontal hull and turret armour of the
Model H. This up-armouring increased the weight of the
Model H to 21.6 tonnes (21.3 tons) and necessitated
modification to the suspension and the introduction of
wider tracks to compensate for the extra load.

The first few hundred vehicles of the next variant, the
Model J, possessed a better level of protection thanks to
their integral (rather than added on) 50mm- (2in-) thick
frontal armour, even if this version still mounted the same
5cm L/42 gun as had its immediate predecessors. Later
Model J vehicles with the new designation Sdkfz 141/1,
however, were much more potent vehicles in that they
mounted the formidable long-barrelled (60-calibres long)

ABOVE *The Red Army extensively used captured German armoured
fighting vehicles. Here, Soviet crews operate an early Panzer III Model J
which retains the shorter 5cm L/42 gun unlike later Model J tanks.
The hull machine-gun is fitted in the new Kugelblende 50 ball mounting.*

5cm KwK 39 L/60 gun. Even though this vehicle carried
fewer main armament rounds – 84 instead of 99 – to
compensate for the heavier gun, the weight of the L/60-
armed Model J still rose to 22.3 tonnes (21.9 tons). This
vehicle was by far the most widely produced version of all
the Panzer IIIs, with German firms delivering 2516 of these
vehicles to the German Army at an average monthly rate of
148 tanks during a 17-month long production run between
March 1941 and July 1942.

The next version, the Model L, was very similar to the
Model J except that it sported a modified suspension to
compensate for the fact that the new long 5cm L/60 gun
had made the Model J vehicle rather nose heavy. The Model
L also possessed enhanced levels of protection through
spaced armour that absorbed enemy rounds more
effectively than homogeneous armour. Once again, to offset
the heavier weight of this spaced armour, the tank carried
only 78 main armament rounds, just over half the armament

that was carried in the original Model A tank. German factories produced a total of 703 of these Model L tanks during a seven-month period between June and December 1942.

The next variant, the Model M, which entered service in late 1942, incorporated minor modifications to simplify construction and thus boost the rate at which German firms produced the tank. This version also possessed the novel thin armour side skirting (Schürzen) to protect its wheels and tracks from hollow-charge, anti-tank weapons. German factories delivered 292 Model M vehicles over a five-month period between October 1942 and February 1943 at an average rate of 58 tanks per month.

Sturmpanzer III – Model N

The final version of the Panzer III, the Model N (Sdkfz 141/2), first entered service in late 1942. This vehicle was similar to its predecessor the Model M, except that it mounted the short-barrelled (24-calibre) 7.5cm gun previously fitted in Panzer IV tanks before 1942. This gun had a poor anti-tank performance, but was ideal for the heavy close-fire support role for which the Model N was intended, a role reflected in the vehicle's popular name, the Sturmpanzer III assault tank.

German factories delivered 666 Model N tanks in total, 447 in late 1942 and the balance (219), during the first eight

months of 1943, after which time the Germans terminated all Panzer III construction. The High Command then transferred these production resources to the manufacture of the heavier Panzer IV tank and the quicker-to-build StuG III assault gun; for what Germany desperately needed in 1943 was to deliver the maximum number of armoured fighting vehicles as quickly as possible to the frontline troops to offset the very large losses incurred by these forces.

Production Rates

Between 1936 and August 1943, German factories constructed 6123 Panzer III tanks, with all but 200 delivered during the war. Some 673 of these tanks mounted the 3.7cm gun, 2815 the short 5cm gun, 1969 mounted the long-barrelled version of this weapon, and the remainder the short 75mm gun. German firms also produced an additional 9500 Panzer III chassis as platforms for various other armoured fighting vehicles. Panzer III production picked up during 1941 when 1703 tanks were completed, after the German Army Tank Committee set a production target of

BELOW *A column of German armour belonging to the 5th SS Panzergrenadier Division* Wiking *during the German summer offensive of 1942 on the Eastern Front. The distinctive bolt-on armour on the upper hull rear of tank 211 identifies it as a Panzer III Model H.*

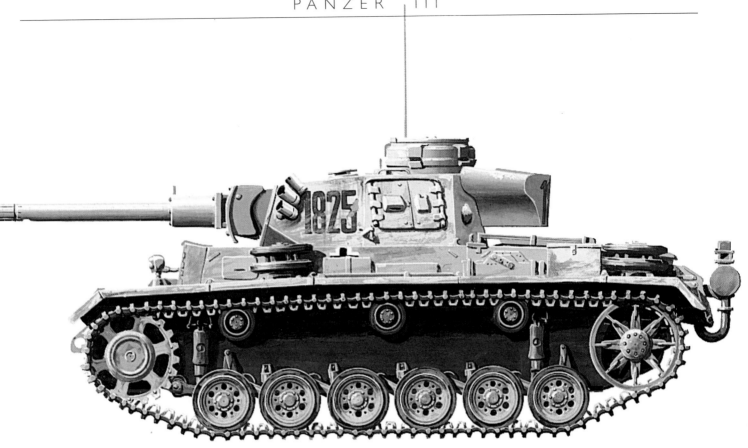

7992 Panzer III tanks – almost double the current German tank strength! This figure was based on the requirements of a 36-division panzer force, set by Hitler as an ultimate goal. Attempts to fulfil these Herculean targets pushed Panzer III production to a peak during 1942, when 2608 tanks were completed.

The Germans possessed just 98 Panzer III tanks during the Polish Campaign, although this figure had risen to 349 by the invasion of the West. During 1941, the new Panzer III Model G tank with its 5cm L/42 gun demonstrated its tactical worth both during the German occupation of the Balkans in April, and more importantly in Operation 'Barbarossa'. On 22 June 1941, the opening day of 'Barbarossa', the Wehrmacht possessed 2501 Panzer III tanks, of which 1174 were Model G, H and early J tanks that mounted the 5cm L/42 gun. In both the East and in North Africa between late 1941 and early 1943, the Panzer III Models J–M with their long 5cm L/60 guns remained the premier vehicles of the German panzer force. From late 1943, however, the Germans steadily withdrew this now outclassed tank type from frontline service.

Submersible Tanks

German firms also produced several types of specialised vehicles based on the Panzer III tank, including several dozen Model F–H vehicles that were converted into Tauchpanzer (Diving Panzer) III submersible tanks for Operation 'Sealion', the projected German invasion of Britain. German factories sealed all openings on these tanks, fitted rubber sheets to provide water-tight protection to key parts of the vehicle, and installed an 18m- (59ft-) long breathing tube for the crew. These measures enabled the Tauchpanzer III to wade through water up to 15m (49ft) deep. The four special panzer battalions that deployed these vehicles formed the spearhead of the projected invasion force. The Germans never carried out Operation 'Sealion', however, and subsequently allocated these tanks to the 18th Panzer Division for Operation 'Barbarossa'. On 22 June 1941, these vehicles drove across the bottom of the River Lessna, a tributary of the River Bug, in the first river crossing by submerged tanks in World War II.

Command Tanks

German firms also produced five command tank variants based on the Panzer III. The first three, the Befehlswagen

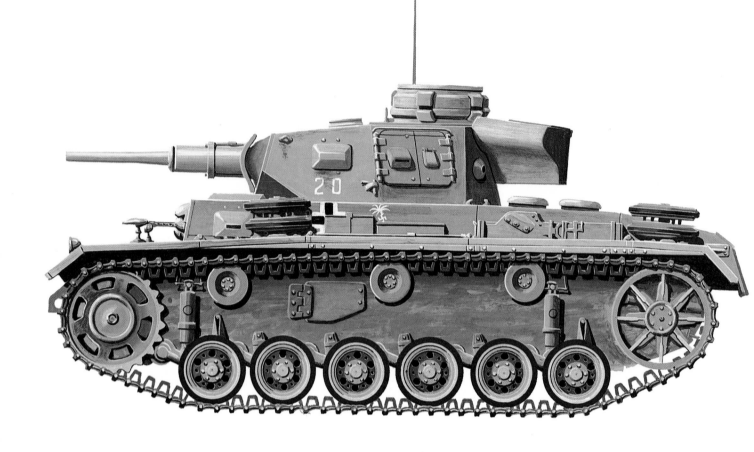

(Armoured Command Vehicle) III Models D1, E and H, were slightly modified Panzer III vehicles that mounted a prominent rail antenna for their powerful communications systems. German factories constructed 30 Model D1 command tanks during 1938–39, 45 Model E vehicles in 1939–40 and 175 Model H command variants between November 1940 and January 1942. The Germans also produced a further 131 Panzer III command tanks, designated the Model J and Model M between August 1942 and February 1943, some of which continued in frontline service until 1945.

The Panzer III was the mainstay of the German tank forces on the Eastern Front from 1941 until early 1943, and contributed greatly to the early successes which the Germans were able to achieve against the Red Army. Yet the German Army's disconcerting experiences at the hands of the formidable new Soviet T34 and KV tanks in the summer of 1941 made it clear that, in the not too distant future, the Panzer III would soon fail to meet to the requirements of armoured warfare on the Eastern Front. Despite this growing battlefield inferiority, production of the Panzer III peaked during 1942, as the Germans became desperate to deliver the maximum number of new tanks to replace heavy battlefield losses. Indeed, it was only in the summer

ABOVE *An early production example of the Panzer III Model J that is distinguishable from later Model Js by its 5cm L/42 gun. This tank sports a desert camouflage scheme. The palm-tree-with-swastika symbol on the hull sides identifies the parent formation as Rommel's famous Africa Corps.*

of 1943 that the Germans terminated Panzer III production in favour of easily constructed assault guns and more powerful tanks. By late 1943, the Panzer III was virtually obsolete and the German Army phased it out of frontline service, although it retained 700 vehicles for employment in garrison, internal security or training units.

The Panzer III in Combat

That the Panzer III did not make an even more significant contribution to the late 1939 Axis triumph in Poland was not due to inherent weaknesses in the tank's performance but rather because of the small numbers of this tank which were available to the German forces at this time; of the 3363 German tanks available for the invasion of Poland, just 98 of these were Panzer III vehicles.

Despite their rarity, however, these Panzer III tanks played a crucial role in the campaign supplementing the firepower of the lightly armed Panzer I and II tanks. The more potent firepower of the 37mm-armed Panzer III was crucial to ensure the continued momentum of the armoured Blitzkrieg spearheads as they swiftly thrust into the Polish rear areas. A greater proportionate casualty rate was experienced by the Panzer III during the Polish campaign than any other German tank, with one-quarter (26 out of 98) of them being lost. Given that the Panzer III was better armoured than many other German tanks, the heavy losses this vehicle suffered attest to the great reliance the Germans placed on this tank in Poland.

The Panzer III came into its own during Operation 'Barbarossa'. The Germans employed 965 Panzer III tanks for the attack out of a total tank deployment of 3332 vehicles, making it the most numerous tank type to be committed to the invasion. The Panzer III was crucial to the momentous German successes achieved during the first months of 'Barbarossa'. Many Panzer III tanks deployed for this operation mounted the 5cm L/42 gun, while a few Model H and some early J vehicles possessed enhanced armour protection. These Panzer III tanks proved highly effective against the vast majority of Soviet tanks, which the Germans were able to destroy in their hundreds during the first weeks of the operation. The German 5cm L/42 gun, for example, could penetrate 47mm- (1.9in-) thick armour at 450m (1476ft).

Soviet Superiority

However, it was not long before the German Army engaged the Soviet's newest and most formidable tanks and the weakness of all Germany's panzer models, save the Panzer IV, became

RIGHT *Right arm just visible, SS General Paul 'Papa' Hausser in the commander's cupola of a late production Panzer III Model J in Kharkov in March 1943. Note the divisional emblem on the tank, indicating it is a panzer of the 2nd SS Panzer Division* Das Reich.

clear. The Soviet T34 medium and KV1 heavy tanks were both armed with the 7.62cm gun at a time when the Germans were just up-gunning from the 3.7cm to the 5cm gun. The KV1 was protected by 90mm (3.6in) armour, twice that of the German tanks, while the well-sloped 45mm- (1.8in-) thick armour of the T34 gave it a level of protection which was close to that of its heavier cousin. Consequently, both these Soviet tanks were virtually immune to fire from German 3.7cm and 5cm L/42 tank guns at normal combat ranges.

This dangerous superiority became abundantly clear on 22 June 1941, when the Germans engaged the KV1 for the first time. The Soviet XIV Tank Corps counter-attacked the advance made by the Panzer 35(t) tanks of the 6th Panzer Division. With the exception of the 8.8cm anti-aircraft gun, pressed into use as an anti-tank weapon, all other German tank and anti-tank guns failed to penetrate the armour of the

KV1. The Germans only managed to knock out one of these tanks, after scoring eight hits from an 8.8cm anti-aircraft gun.

The Soviets further demonstrated the superiority of the T34 and the KV1 in subsequent engagements. In the Ukraine, for example, one T34 continued firing after taking an incredible 24 hits from German 3.7cm rounds. At Mtsensk, near Orel, on 4 October 1941, the spearhead of the 4th Panzer Division had just secured a bridgehead over the River Lisiza near Kamenewa when the Soviets counter-attacked. Some 50 Red Army T34 and KV1 tanks lay concealed in a wood near Woin, waiting for the Germans to reach the top of the crest beyond the river. The Soviet ambush knocked out 10 Panzer III tanks and drove the 4th Panzer Division back across the Lisiza. At ranges of 800m (2624ft) all the rounds fired by Panzer III tanks which were equipped with the 5cm L/42 gun simply bounced off the frontal armour of the KV1.

The shock caused by these early disastrous encounters prompted the Germans to incorporate the long-barrelled 5cm L/60 gun and enhanced 60mm- (2.4in-) thick armour

ABOVE *The crew of a Panzer III Model J pose for this picture during a rare lull in the savage fighting that characterised the German early July 1943 'Citadel' Offensive at Kursk. This vehicle's number indicates that it is the first tank in the second troop of the regimental staff company.*

into subsequent Panzer III models. These experiences also led the Germans to begin development of the new medium Panzer V Panther tank and the heavy Panzer VI Tiger I.

The Later Version Model J Panzer

In April 1942, Rommel's Africa Corps was reinforced by later-version Panzer III Model J tanks with their long (L/60) 5cm gun and 5cm- (2.4in-) thick integral armour protection. These vehicles were superior not just to all Allied tanks at that time deployed in North Africa, but also to the M3 Grant tanks that arrived one month later. The Germans employed these tanks effectively during the Gazala battles of June 1942 and were able to inflict heavy losses on the British forces. By the time of General Montgomery's successful Allied counter-attack at El Alamein in October–November

1942, however, the superiority of the Model J had been eroded by the arrival of the new Allied Sherman tank.

The Demise of the Panzer III

Throughout 1942, on the Eastern Front and in North Africa, the German Army relied heavily on the Panzer III Models G–L. By mid-1943, however, even the latest Panzer III Model M and N tanks were outclassed and the Germans phased the vehicle out of frontline service. By October 1943, only five panzer divisions on the Eastern Front still deployed more than one company of Panzer III tanks. Moreover, continued attrition, together with redeployment to security duties, meant that by mid-1944, these tanks were virtually extinct in frontline panzer divisions, which were now equipped as standard with a battalion each of Panzer IV and Panther tanks. Several panzer divisions, though, still employed a few Panzer III tanks.

As late as 27 June 1944, the 12th Panzer Division fielded nine Panzer III Model J and M tanks during its desperate attempt to stem the Soviet onslaught in Operation 'Bagration', the Red Army's offensive of summer 1944. Furthermore, a total of 150 Bergepanzer III recovery vehicles and 80 Panzer III Model M command tanks also remained in frontline German service throughout 1944. The German Army deployed small numbers of both vehicles during their Ardennes counter-offensive in December 1944, and Allied aircraft knocked out at least one Panzer III command tank during these operations.

By mid-1944, however, the Germans deployed most of the remaining 700 Panzer III tanks in the training units that doubled up as garrison troops in the various parts of Europe still occupied by the Germans. The number of Panzer III tanks employed by these units varied widely, ranging from the 70 tanks fielded by the Panzer Brigade Norway, to the solitary Panzer III deployed in addition to various captured French vehicles in the 100th Panzer Replacement and Training Battalion stationed in Normandy. During 1944–45 the German Army even committed these garrison units into combat as the Allies advanced into the Reich itself. Indeed, combat losses reduced these 700 Panzer III tanks to just 166 vehicles by 1 April 1945, including 50 tanks still stationed in Norway and just one solitary vehicle augmenting German resistance in the encircled Nazi-controlled enclave of northwestern Holland. It is evident that even obsolete German tanks went down fighting in the cataclysm that engulfed the German Army and Third Reich in the last months of World War II.

RIGHT *A Panzer III Model M tank belonging to the 6th Company of an unidentified mechanised formation during the 1944 Italian campaign. Note the additional curved armour added to the turret sides upon which the vehicle's number has been painted. This gave protection against hollow-charge anti-tank rounds.*

CHAPTER 9

STURMGESCHÜTZ III

Originally designed for the infantry close support role, assault guns, such as the StuG III, were increasingly used by the German Army – after being up-gunned – in the anti-tank role to counter-measure Soviet armour. Thousands of these armoured fighting vehicles were produced, giving the German Army an effective weapon against the hordes of Russian tanks in the East.

The origins of the Sturmgeschütz (assault gun) lay in demands made in the mid-1930s by the German artillery branch for an armoured close-infantry support vehicle. The artillery arm firmly believed that such a vehicle was a necessity, since German military thought called for the strategic concentration of all available armour solely in mechanised formations. The German Army Weapons Department issued a development contract in June 1936 with the far-sighted stipulation that such a vehicle should possess a low silhouette for better survivability and a dual armour-piercing and high-explosive capability. The High Command selected Daimler-Benz to design and produce a prototype vehicle, and contracted Krupp to develop and install an appropriate main armament.

Development History

The vehicle that emerged in the late 1930s was armed with the short-barrelled 7.5cm KwK4 L/24 gun then being installed in the new Panzer IV medium/heavy tank. The requirement for a low silhouette, however, precluded mounting the main armament in a revolving turret, or even in an open armoured shield as in subsequent German self-propelled anti-tank guns. Instead, a main gun with limited traverse was mounted in a fixed superstructure installed directly onto the chassis of the Panzer III tank. This arrangement enabled the vehicle's height to be reduced to just 1.95m (6ft 5in) in comparison with the 2.5m (8ft 3in) height of the Panzer III tank. The vehicle possessed 50mm- (2in-) thick armour on the front, 43mm (1.7in) on the sides and 11mm (0.4in) on the roof, which provided it with better

LEFT The early production StuG III Model G incorporated a roof-mounted machine gun protected by an armoured shell, but lacked the distinctive Saukopf (pig's head) mantlet of later versions. These assault guns belong to the 16th SS Panzergrenadier Division Reichsführer-SS.

ABOVE *German soldiers crouch down for shelter behind the rear superstructure of an early StuG III, which was equipped with the short-barrelled 7.5cm StuK 37 L/24 gun. Note the extremely low silhouette of this vehicle.*

protection than either the Panzer III or IV. Having designed a new type of armoured fighting vehicle, the Germans, designated the vehicle as an assault gun (Sturmgeschütz) to reflect its intended role to provide fire support for attacking infantry.

This assault gun design proved a valuable infantry support vehicle which subsequently became – when up-gunned – a potent anti-tank weapon. Daimler-Benz chose the chassis of the Panzer III tank as the basis of the assault gun in order to take the projected 20-tonne (19.7-ton) weight of the vehicle. Once the German Army had accepted the Daimler-Benz design, it designated the vehicle the 7.5cm-armed Armoured Self-Propelled Assault Gun III (Sdkfz 142), although the vehicle quickly became popularly known by the abbreviated title of StuG III.

Lacking a turret, the assault gun needed only a four-man crew. Designed primarily as a close-support weapon, the vehicle carried 84 rounds of ammunition that comprised 55 high-explosive and eight smoke shells, but only 21 armour-piercing rounds. The short 7.5cm gun possessed a modest muzzle velocity of 420 metres per second (1378 feet per second), and when firing armour-piercing shells could penetrate just 40mm (1.6in) of 30-degree sloped armour at 1094m (3589ft) – a relatively poor anti-tank capability.

Daimler-Benz constructed 30 pre-production StuG III vehicles during the spring of 1940 and equipped five experimental batteries, one of which saw limited service in the latter stages of the Western Campaign during early June 1940. The success of the vehicle in France prompted the Germans to commence full-scale production in July 1940 with a target output rate of 50 vehicles per month to be reached by September 1940. The first production model, the StuG III Model A, only differed from the pre-production vehicles in that it was powered by a larger 320bhp Maybach HL 120 TR engine. Initial production of the Model A was undertaken exclusively by Alkett but from 1943 both MIAG and Daimler-Benz joined assault gun construction. Early production difficulties ensured that the target delivery rate was not reached and German factories completed only 184 StuG III vehicles during the second half of 1940, at an average rate of 30 units per month.

Late in 1940, the Model B entered service and during 1941 successive variants, the Models C, D and E, went into production with only minor modifications. All these vehicles were fitted with a new six-speed Aphon synchromesh gearbox. A drawback of all these early StuG III models was that they lacked a machine gun for local defence. Moreover, an increased rate of Panzer III production during 1941 reduced the availability of suitable chassis, which ensured that German firms completed only 548 StuG III vehicles during that year. The German experience of encountering enemy heavy armour after the invasion of the Soviet Union in the summer of 1941, made it apparent that the Germans needed greater and more mobile anti-tank capability. Despite its infantry-support role, the StuG III was an obvious contender to meet this need. Consequently, on 28 September 1941 Hitler ordered that the vehicle be up-armoured and rearmed with a longer-barrelled 7.5cm gun to give it a genuine anti-tank capability, all regardless of the

SPECIFICATIONS: Sturmgeschütz III Model A (Sdkfz142)

GENERAL
Vehicle Type: self-propelled assault gun
Entered Service: spring 1940
Crew: four
Combat Weight: 21.3 tonnes
(21 tons)

DIMENSIONS
Overall Length: 5.41m (17 ft 9in)
Overall Width: 2.92m (9ft 7in)
Height: 1.95m (6ft 5in)

ARMAMENT
Main: 7.5cm (3in) StuK 37 L/24 gun
Main Gun Traverse: 12.5 degrees left to 12.5 degrees right
Secondary: none

AMMUNITION STOWAGE
Main: 84 rounds
Secondary: n/a

ARMOUR
Hull Front (Nose): 50mm (2.0in)
(at 69 degrees)
Hull Front (Driver's Plate): 50mm
(2.0in) (at 80 degrees)
Hull Sides: 30mm (1.2in) (at 90 degrees)
Hull Rear: 8mm (0.3in) (at 60-80 degrees)
Superstructure Front: 50mm (2.0in)
(at 75 degrees)
Superstructure Sides: 30mm (1.2in)
(at 90 degrees)
Superstructure Rear: 30mm (1.2in)
(at 60 degrees)

Superstructure Roof: 8mm (0.3in)
(at 0-12 degrees)

MOTIVE POWER
Engine: Maybach HL 120 TRM V12-cylinder petrol
Power: 300 bhp
Fuel Capacity: 320 litres (70 gallons)

PERFORMANCE
Maximum Road Speed: 45kph (28mph)
Maximum Cross-Country Speed:
19kph (12mph)
Operational Range (Road): 161km
(100 miles)
Operational Range (Cross-Country):
97km (60 miles)

resulting weight increase and consequent reduction in speed. The Weapons Department contracted Daimler-Benz to develop this new vehicle using a modified superstructure designed by Rheinmetall-Borsig. The completed prototype was shown to Hitler on 31 March 1942 and went into production as the StuG III Model F during late spring. The vehicle mounted the longer-barrelled (43-calibres long) 7.5cm Assault Cannon (StuK 40 L/43) as its main armament, which necessitated some modification to the front superstructure. The larger gun also increased the vehicle's weight to 21.6 tonnes (21.3 tons). German factories produced a total of 120 StuG III Model F assault guns.

The next variant, the Model G, mounted an even longer-barrelled version of the same gun, the 7.5cm StuK 40 L/48, a main armament that would be retained in all subsequent assault gun production. Unlike the L/43 gun of the Model F, the longer L/48 gun of the Model G included a muzzle brake. The additional barrel length increased the gun's muzzle velocity to 770 m/s (2525 f/s) and its effective range to 2188m (7178ft) when firing armour-piercing shells. The gun could penetrate 91mm (3.6in) of 30-degree sloped armour and 109mm (4.3in) of unsloped armour at

1000m (3280ft). Its elevation ranged from -5 degrees to +20 degrees and its horizontal traverse was 20 degrees. The Model G was also the first StuG III variant to possess a 7.92mm MG 34 machine gun for local defence. The Model G was also better protected, mainly through the addition of 30mm- (1.2in-) thick appliqué plates bolted onto the basic 50mm (2in) hull frontal armour. The side and top armour was also increased to 30mm (1.2in) and 20mm (0.8in), respectively, and from 1943 armoured side skirts (Schürzen) were fitted to provide protection against hollow-charge weapons. These modifications increased the weight of the Model G to 24 tonnes (23.6 tons).

With production standardised on this model, and with several new firms brought in, assault gun production blossomed. Hitler set an ambitious construction target of 220 Model G vehicles per month to be achieved by June 1943. During the next year the Führer again raised projected output levels to 300 units per month. Not only were these targets met, but they were exceeded. German factories produced 3041 StuG III vehicles during 1943, 4850 in 1944, but just 123 during early 1945. Increased production rates were facilitated both by the termination of Panzer III construction in August 1943, after which the chassis was built exclusively for the StuG III, and by progressive simplification of the construction process. Such time-saving modifications included the use of a partially cast superstructure and a cast iron Saukopf (Pig's Head) gun mantlet with 50mm (2in) armour that replaced the previous

BELOW *A StuG III fulfils its original purpose – as an infantry close support vehicle. Here it provides intimate support for an infantry squad advancing into a Soviet village. The autumn rains have transformed the ground into a quagmire. Note the missing right hand light on the hull front.*

bolted box-mantlet on earlier variants. The Model G also underwent a series of minor modifications during its production run, including the enhancement of its protection from late 1943, not by increasing its armour thickness, but by interlocking the bow plates to provide greater strength. From spring 1944, 15mm- (0.6in-) thick concrete was also added to the front of the superstructure for extra protection.

From 1943, some 10 percent of assault gun production was diverted to a new assault howitzer variant that mounted a 28-calibre long 10.5cm assault howitzer (StuH 42 L/28) in place of the 7.5cm gun. This vehicle entered production in small numbers in late 1942 in an infantry support role as the German Army increasingly diverted the StuG III to an anti-tank function. Officially designated the 10.5cm Assault Howitzer 1942 (Sturm-Haubitze 42), the vehicle was commonly known as the StuH 42. The vehicle mounted an electrically fired version of the standard German 10.5cm 1918 light field howitzer fitted with a muzzle brake. This 2.95m- (9 ft 8in-) long gun, which possessed a traverse of 20 degrees and an elevation of from -6 degrees to +20 degrees, could achieve a muzzle velocity of 540 m/s (1770 f/s). Like early versions of the StuG III, the StuH 42 possessed no machine gun for local defence. Due to the relatively small size of the chassis and the bulk of the 105mm howitzer, only 36 rounds could be carried. The vehicle thus had enhanced

ABOVE *The StuG III Models C and D incorporated a modified superstructure. The vehicle belongs to an unidentified unit with a distinctive animal insignia. One drawback of these models was the lack of a machine gun for local defence.*

high-explosive capability at the expense of its armour-piercing performance – a situation that reflected the original infantry support role for which the Germans had designed the assault gun.

The earliest StuH 42 vehicles were built on the Panzer III Model F chassis but subsequent vehicles were generally based on the Model G chassis. German factories produced nine StuH 42 vehicles during late 1942, 204 in 1943, and 904 during 1944, with production ceasing at the end of that year. Although early production vehicles carried a muzzle brake for increased range and performance this feature was deleted during 1944 in the interests of economy. Even though the weight of the StuH 42 increased to 24.5 tonnes (24.1 tons) thanks to its larger gun, the vehicle's performance generally mirrored that of the StuG III Model G.

With significant resources being diverted into assault gun production by the middle of the war, and given the numerous competing authorities that existed in Nazi Germany, it was perhaps inevitable that a bitter struggle should develop for control of these vehicles. After Hitler appointed General Heinz Guderian as Inspector-General of

ABOVE *A StuG III provides close support for a German infantry squad as it advances through the ruined suburbs of Stalingrad in late 1942. This battle degenerated into house-to-house fighting to gain just yards of ground in the rubble of what had once been the urban centre of the city.*

Armoured Forces in the spring of 1943, a three-way contest for control of the assault gun arm ensued between Guderian's panzer arm, the infantry branch, and the artillery. Guderian attempted to augment Germany's waning tank strength by incorporating assault guns into his understrength panzer units. The struggle ended in a compromise: Hitler diverted some StuG III assault guns to both Guderian's tank forces and select infantry anti-tank battalions, but most StuG III vehicles remained under the control of the artillery until the end of the war.

Given the nature of this compromise, assault guns performed several missions within a variety of different units. Initially, they joined independent assault gun battalions organised into three companies of ten vehicles, plus a battalion commander's vehicle, producing a total of 31 assault guns. By June 1941, the German Army had raised 10 such battalions and deployed them on the Eastern Front. Here, assault guns found themselves increasingly committed to an anti-tank role in support of the thinly stretched German infantry for whom armoured reserves were always scarce. The total number of assault gun battalions in service steadily increased from 19 in July 1942

to 37 by the end of 1943. During 1943–44 the German Army began using assault guns to replace tanks in the individual panzer battalions of the newly raised panzergrenadier divisions. From late 1943, the High Command also began utilising assault guns to equip the new tank destroyer company within the anti-tank battalion found in each of the new 1944-pattern infantry divisions. This measure was necessary because the purpose-built Jagdpanzer IV and 38(t) tank destroyers intended to equip these units were delayed coming off the production lines.

Further developments in the employment of the StuG III materialised during 1944 as Germany's deteriorating strategic position demanded an expanded role for assault guns. During the summer of 1944 the German Army redesignated the 42 assault gun battalions then in service as brigades to reflect both their increasing tactical importance and their independent status. A few also underwent expansion to a new, larger establishment, of 45 assault guns. From late 1944, the German High Command also added organic grenadier platoons to provide intimate infantry support to create new army assault artillery brigades.

A fundamental problem with German assault gun units was that, as independent army troops that were in great demand, the High Command had to transfer them constantly from crisis to crisis to support the overstretched German infantry. But such frequent redeployment prevented development of the familiarity so crucial to effective combined-arms operations. In particular, due to inexperience and unfamiliarity, German infantry rarely were able to provide effective support for assault guns. During 1944, the High Command sought to redress this drawback by adding infantry escort platoons to assault artillery units to provide a modicum of intrinsic infantry protection. This process only proceeded slowly, however, as by 1945 Germany had reached the bottom of its manpower pool. Consequently, on 1 January 1945 the German Army fielded 39 assault gun brigades, but only seven of the expanded assault artillery brigades that possessed organic infantry platoons.

During 1944, the StuG III also saw wider service in the tank regiments of panzer divisions, to offset growing tank shortages. The ubiquitous StuG III was also supplied to Germany's Axis allies – Finland, Romania, Hungary and Bulgaria – to bolster their meagre armoured forces. As assault gun production increased rapidly in late 1944, these vehicles finally outstripped tanks as the most numerous vehicle in the German armoured fighting vehicle inventory. On 1 February 1945, the number of assault guns of all types in German service peaked at 6501, compared to 6191 tanks. Production of all assault gun types plummeted, however,

from 1025 units in December 1944, to just 347 during March 1945. The combination of rapidly declining construction and the catastrophic armoured fighting vehicle losses the Germans suffered in early 1945 meant that the number of operational StuG III vehicles in German service had shrunk to just 943 by 1 April 1945. Even with this massively reduced strength, the StuG III still remained the most common armoured fighting vehicle in German service during the last month of the war.

The StuG III proved a robust, mechanically reliable and effective anti-tank vehicle. Armed with the same gun as the Panzer IV and with similar or even slightly superior armour, the StuG III also benefited from a lower silhouette. Though by 1945 its 75mm gun was barely a match for the new Soviet and Western Allied heavy tanks, the vehicle nevertheless proved a valuable mobile anti-tank weapon until the end of the war. The StuG III, however, suffered from the disadvantage experienced by all German self-propelled

BELOW *A crew with their StuG III – probably a Model F – during a lull in the fighting for Staraya Russiya in the Soviet Union during April 1943. Up-gunned assault guns, such as this, were used to supplement German tanks in the anti-tank role.*

guns, of not possessing a rotating turret. In the defensive role for which the German Army increasingly employed assault guns after 1943 this drawback was not a great handicap. A ubiquitous vehicle – over 9000 were produced, more than any other German armoured fighting vehicle of World War II – the StuG III fought extensively on all fronts.

StuG III in combat

Two German assault gun brigades, the 341st and 394th, fought in the West during the 1944 Normandy Campaign. The StuG III also equipped two companies each of the panzer regiments of the 2nd, 9th and 10th SS Panzer Divisions which served in Normandy, reflecting the progressive substitution of assault guns to offset tank shortages. Furthermore, the tank destroyer battalions of the 1st and 2nd SS Panzer Divisions were also entirely equipped with the StuG III, in place of the Jagdpanzer IV, which had not yet reached field units in any numbers.

It was in the bitter defensive battles of the last year of the war that the StuG III came into its own and revealed its true mettle as a valuable tank killer. But the vehicle also performed well in the few offensive operations undertaken by the Germans during 1944–45. StuG III units participated extensively in the Ardennes counter-offensive of December 1944, where the vehicle's low silhouette and fuel economy made it an obvious choice for operations in the wooded and hilly terrain. One such unit was the 244th Assault Gun Brigade, which distinguished itself by destroying 54 American tanks for the loss of only two assault guns.

One of the most effective assault gun formations in the German Army was the 190th Assault Gun Brigade, which was mentioned twice in German High Command communiqués during defensive fighting in West Prussia in the spring of 1945. One of the first assault gun battalions raised in 1940, this veteran unit had a long and impressive history as a seasoned anti-tank force. On 26 February 1945 alone, the brigade claimed a staggering 104 tank kills for the loss of only four vehicles. Then on 3 March 1945, the brigade passed its one-thousandth tank kill since its debut. This was such an impressive feat that the High Command 'rewarded' the brigade by evacuating it from the encircled German enclave of West Prussia – but only so that it could participate in the final desperate defence of Berlin!

Another distinctive StuG III formation was the 232nd Assault Gun Brigade. During the spring of 1945, this brigade continued to fight despite being cut off in the Samland peninsula in East Prussia. Reinforced by remnants of other shattered brigades, it became the largest German assault gun formation of the war, reaching a strength of some 2000 personnel and 47 assault guns in February 1945. However, the brigade could not withstand overwhelming Soviet numerical superiority, and attrition steadily ate away at its vehicle strength, until by April it had lost its last assault gun. To escape Soviet captivity, on 8 May 1945, the last day of the war, naval barges transported the remnants of the 232nd from Danzig to Hela, from where they were evacuated that night to Denmark aboard a grossly overcrowded torpedo boat.

Assault gun units also played an important role in the defence of the German capital, Berlin, during April 1945.

BELOW *The large, box-like mantlet housing the long-barrelled 7.5cm L/48 gun is evident in this side view of a 1943-produced StuG III Model G, as is the close defence machine gun with protective shield mounted on top of the superstructure roof.*

ABOVE *Troops of the 9SS Panzer Division Hohenstauffen relax by a 1944-version StuG III Model G after victory at Arnhem in late 1944. These much-feared Waffen-SS troops were so impressed by British resistance that they treated prisoners (such as the three here) with great respect.*

A formation then refitting near Berlin was the 243rd Assault Artillery Brigade, one of the few upgraded assault gun formations. An experienced formation shattered in previous defensive fighting, lack of available assault guns forced its deployment as improvised infantry on the Teltow Canal during mid-April. Finally the brigade received 40 brand new assault guns straight off the production line of Alkett's Berlin factory and, on 14-15 April, it joined combat against the American bridgehead over the Elbe River at Schoenebeck. Thereafter, the brigade attempted to relieve Berlin under the command of the newly formed *Theodor Korner* Division raised from training cadres and German Labour Service personnel. The brigade, supported by the Assault Gun Demonstration Brigade Schill (raised from the instructors and recruits of the training school at Burg near Magdeburg), successfully recaptured Treuenbrietzen. Despite displaying élan akin to that so evident during the heady German victories of 1939-41, these units could not break through the powerful Soviet cordon around Berlin to relieve the city and rescue their Führer.

The mission to break into Berlin was achieved, however, by the 249th Assault Gun Brigade in an action that stands out as one of the last triumphs of a German Army then in its death throes. On 24 April, the 249th Brigade's crews collected 31 brand new assault guns directly from the Alkett factory at Spandau, the last vehicles to come off its production line, and then attempted to halt the advancing Red Army spearheads at Spandau. On 27 April, the High

Command ordered the brigade to counter attack in order to break through the recently completed Soviet encirclement of Berlin. Amazingly, the 249th succeeded in smashing through the already formidable Soviet ring and took up defensive positions at Friedrichshain, within the Berlin defensive perimeter. This achievement immediately earned the brigade commander the coveted Knight's Cross. Reduced by 30 April to just nine operational assault guns, the brigade conducted a fighting retreat back to the Alexanderplatz, before it commenced a last stand at the Berlin Technical High School. During the night of 2-3 May, after word arrived of Hitler's suicide and the imminent surrender of the garrison, the remnants of the 249th attempted to break out of Berlin. The brigade's last three operational assault guns spearheaded this desperate escape bid, but these were quickly knocked out and the breakout attempt stalled near Spandau. Incredibly, small groups of assault gun crews, including the brigade commander, managed to evade capture and slipped through the Soviet lines to reach the Elbe River and surrender to American forces. It is evident that during the last days of the war, many assault guns also went down fighting desperately alongside German tanks, against numerically superior Allied forces.

PANZER IV

Steadily up-gunned and up-armoured, the reliable Panzer IV remained in first-line combat service throughout World War II, and represented the work-horse of the Panzer arm for virtually the entire war. It was the only German tank to stay in continuous production throughout the war, and was probably in production longer than any other tank from that war.

The genesis of both the Panzer III and IV – the principal tanks of the German Army during the first half of World War II – stemmed from a conference of the Army Weapons Department on 11 January 1934. This meeting determined what equipment was required for the new, expanded army scheduled to emerge now that the Nazis had come to power. The Weapons Department considered it necessary for German armaments firms to design tanks heavier than the Panzer I and II light training models then under development. During the autumn of 1934, the Inspector-General of Motorised Troops, General Lutz, and his Chief of Staff, Heinz Guderian, concurred on the need for a medium/heavy or close-support tank that

mounted a low-velocity, short-barrelled 7.5cm gun to provide fire support to the lighter tanks within the envisaged future panzer divisions. This gun would provide good high-explosive capability, though at the expense of anti-tank performance. Given the weight limits of existing German road bridges, the Weapons Department stipulated that this proposed heavy tank, designated the VK2000, should weigh no more than 24 tonnes (23.6 tons). The High Command promptly redesignated this project with the camouflage title BW (for Bataillonsführerwagen – battalion commander's vehicle) to disguise German tank production at a time when the arms limitation provisions of the Treaty of Versailles were still theoretically in force.

Development History

During 1934, the firms of Rheinmetall-Borsig, Krupp and MAN each forwarded a prototype BW design, but the Weapons Department rejected each one as unsuitable. Both

LEFT *The crew of this Panzer IV have removed the vehicle's engine, located in the hull rear, in order to carry out essential maintenance. Note the two large hatches in the hull rear decking that have been opened to give access to the engine.*

the Krupp and MAN designs utilised sophisticated interleaved suspension systems that the High Command deemed too experimental to be pursued. The following year, Krupp submitted a prototype for the ZW medium tank development project that ultimately produced the Panzer III tank. Krupp's unsuccessful ZW prototype subsequently became the basis for the firm's 1936 prototype BW/Panzer vehicle, which the Weapons Department this time accepted. Krupp incorporated design features from all three of the original unsuccessful BW prototypes into this vehicle to create the first pre-production model, the 1/BW, later redesignated the Panzer IV Model A. In particular, the new vehicle included the coupled leaf spring suspension of the original Krupp ZW prototype.

The Panzer IV, which remained in production throughout World War II, became the most numerous of all the German wartime tanks. Though it was never intended to be the mainstay of the tank force, the basic design proved so sound and reliable that it was capable of being extensively updated to keep abreast of changing combat and technological developments, without the need for a fundamental redesign. It thus evolved into the premier combat tank of the German Army of World War II.

ABOVE *The first Panzer IV, the Model A, entered service in 1936. Only 35 of this developmental design were produced, identifiable both by the internal mantlet and the uneven frontal plate with the wireless operator's plate (including hull machine-gun) set further back than the driver's plate.*

Nonetheless, at the outset the Germans experienced considerable production difficulties with the Panzer IV, as lack of expertise in building medium/heavy tanks, as well as lack of assembly facilities, ensured that it was slow to come into production. Initially, therefore, it was built only in small pre-production batches.

Special Features

Among the most distinctive features of the Panzer IV Model A was its superstructure which overhung the hull sides. This allowed for subsequent up-gunning and ample internal stowage – including 122 rounds for the 7.5cm KwK L/24 gun. The tank's ammunition for its main armament comprised high-explosive and smoke rounds to provide infantry fire support, plus small quantities of armour-piercing shell. The vehicle also carried two 7.92mm MG 34 machine guns, one mounted coaxially next to the main armament and the other in the hull front, with stowage for 2000 rounds of machine-gun ammunition. The turret also had electrical traverse, power being supplied by a small secondary motor.

The suspension of the Model A – which became standard on all Panzer IV variants – consisted of four bogies on either side, each of which carried two small 470mm (18.5in) rubber-tyred wheels supported by four return rollers, a front drive socket and a rear idler on both sides. German factories completed the first batch of 35 1/BW (Panzer IV Model A) tanks in 1936 and these were used for trials and training. The vehicles, operated by a five-man crew, were powered by a 250bhp V12-cylinder Maybach HL 108 TR petrol engine, and weighed 17.3 tonnes (17 tons) – well within the original weight ceiling. The Model A could reach a top road speed of 30kph (18mph), and possessed an effective operational range of 140km (87 miles) by road and 90km (56 miles) cross-country. The main factor contributing to the lower-than-specified weight of the Model A was its relatively light protection of just 14.5mm- (0.6in-) thick armour plate on the hull and 20mm (0.8in) on the turret.

Other Variants

The next variant, the Panzer IV Model B, entered limited production during 1937 when 45 were built, and these vehicles saw action in Poland in 1939. This variant possessed enhanced protection with 30mm- (1.2in-) thick frontal hull armour that raised the vehicle's weight to 17.7 tonnes (17.4 tons). A larger 320bhp Maybach HL 120 TR engine powered the Model B to compensate for the vehicle's increased weight, which was kept within reasonable limits by reducing main armament ammunition stowage to just 80 rounds.

During 1938–39, the first production model – the Panzer IV Model C – entered service, though again construction was limited and subject to delay. Nonetheless, the 140 Model C vehicles which were built provided the bulk of the Panzer IV force in Poland, a number which was sufficient to provide a medium/heavy tank allocation to support the Panzer I, II and III tanks. The new model differed from its predecessor in that it possessed enhanced 30mm (1.2in) frontal turret armour, and a single-sheet frontal hull plate.

BELOW *The Nationalist Socialist Motor Corps (NSKK) carried out preliminary tank training for German crews before their induction into the Wehrmacht. Here, a trainee crew practises with an outclassed 1938–9 vintage Panzer IV Model C during April 1944.*

ABOVE *A Panzer IV takes up an ambush position in a wood somewhere in the Soviet Union. Once the German crew had covered the vehicle with branches and foliage, it would have been extremely difficult for Red Army forces to detect.*

In the late summer of 1939, the Panzer IV Model D (Sdkfz 161) went into production. This variant incorporated many minor modifications, including increased rear and side armour of 20mm- (0.8in-) thickness, which raised the vehicle's weight to 20 tonnes (17.7 tons). German factories had produced 45 Model D tanks by the start of the Polish Campaign and eventually constructed a total of 248 vehicles before production of the new Model E superseded it during December 1940.

On the Model E, the nose plate armour was increased to a thickness of 50mm (2in) and extra appliqué armour plate was bolted to the sides, as well as to the driver's plate, to enhance protection. The Model E also incorporated a new type of visor as well as a new commander's cupola. Combat experience in Poland and France demonstrated that the vehicle was basically sound and in the summer of 1940 it was officially designated the Panzer IV (Sdfkz 161), the previous camouflage designations being dropped. In the West in 1940, the tank's 7.5cm gun proved valuable against Anglo-French heavy tanks (the French Char B and the British Matilda II), which smaller calibre German tank guns had difficulty penetrating. The campaign also highlighted that most Allied light/medium tanks found it difficult to destroy the more recent Panzer IV models, with their enhanced levels of protection. Krupp manufactured 223 Panzer IV Model E vehicles before the Model F1 entered service in February 1941. Increased production reflected the valuable role the Panzer IV could provide alongside the Panzer III. During 1941, German factories also retro-fitted those older

Panzer IV vehicles, which were returned to workshops for overhaul or repair, to Model F specifications.

Significant Modifications

The Panzer IV Model F1 was the first of the up-armoured variants developed in response to the heavy Anglo-French tanks first encountered in the West during May–June 1940. The significantly modified F1 tank first saw service against the British in North Africa during 1941. The vehicle's armour was fundamentally redesigned with single-sheet armour plate of an increased 50mm- (2in-) thickness on all frontal surfaces and 30mm (1.2in) on the sides, which replaced the bolted appliqué armour retro-fitted to earlier vehicles. A new ball machine-gun mount was also fitted to allow for better local defence, and the driver's visor was once again modified. The increased 22.3 tonne (21.9 ton) weight of the Model F1 forced the Germans to fit newly designed wider 400mm (16in) tracks and a widened front sprocket to minimise increases in the vehicle's ground pressure statistics, in order to maintain its maximum road speed at 42 kph (26 mph).

Limited production of the Model F1 continued at Krupp during 1941. By the time of the invasion of the Soviet Union,

ABOVE *The Model D was the first Panzer IV designed to mount the short 7.5cm gun in a movable external mantlet. This variant reintroduced the staggered hull driver's plate, which had been abandoned after the Model A design.*

the High Command was able to deploy 548 Panzer IV tanks of all types. The demand for new tanks grew enormously and Panzer IV production increased accordingly with a total of 975 Panzer IV Model F1 tanks being completed.

In March 1942, German factories commenced modification of the later tanks in the Panzer IV Model F production run to take the longer-barrelled (43-calibres long) 7.5cm gun KwK 40 gun. Tanks thus equipped were designated the Model F2, although Commonwealth forces, which first encountered the vehicle in the desert during the spring of 1942, termed it the Mark IV Special. In the winter 1941–42, the Germans encountered increasing numbers of the superior Soviet T34 medium and KV1 heavy tanks. This prompted them to radically up-gun the Panzer IV, the only tank then in German service capable of such enhancement, to produce the Model F2. Fitted with the powerful longer gun, this Panzer IV variant was significantly more potent than its predecessors, and it soon proved itself to be both a match for the T34 and superior to the British cruiser tanks encountered in North Africa. The longer gun fielded by the Model F2 possessed a muzzle velocity of 740 metres per second (2428 feet per second) and could penetrate an impressive 89mm (3.5in) of 30 degree-sloped armour at 1000m (3028ft), sufficient to penetrate the frontal armour of the T34 at that distance. Mounting the longer gun, however, again raised the vehicle's weight, this time to 23.6 tonnes (23.2 tons), with a consequent reduction in its top speed to 40kph (25mph).

In 1942, the first Panzer IV Model G vehicles entered service. The basic Model G vehicle weighed the same as the F2, but possessed slightly increased protection and an improved double-baffle muzzle brake on the main armament. German factories incorporated many

refinements into the Model G vehicle during its production run, the most notable of which was the introduction of a longer 48-calibre 7.5cm gun in late 1942, which increased muzzle velocity to 751 metres per second (2461 feet per second). Other design changes included retro-fitting both additional bolted appliqué armour and later 5–9mm- (0.2–0.4in-) thick armoured side skirting (Schürzen) to deflect hollow-charge anti-tank rounds. Under intense pressure from the High Command to boost production rates, German firms constructed 1724 Panzer IV Model F and G tanks during 1942. Simultaneously these factories also upgraded, to Model G standards, many older Panzer IV variants when they were returned to Germany for major repairs.

Model H–J Tanks

In March 1943, the Model H superseded the Model G in service. The basic vehicle, like its predecessor, saw repeated minor design alterations during its production run. This variant was the first to leave the factory treated with

BELOW *Panzer IVs in Russia. Note the tank on the left fitted with side skirts (Schürzen). These were made of mild steel boiler plating, lightly secured, either by spot welding or by hooks on rails, and were intended to protect the tank against hollow-charge projectiles.*

Zimmerit anti-magnetic mine paste, which left an uneven cement-like surface on the vehicle. The Model H tank possessed 80mm- (3.2in-) thick armour as standard on its hull nose-plates. The tank's side and rear armour were 30mm (1.2in) and 20mm (0.8in) thick, respectively, while both the turret front and gun mantlet possessed 50mm (2in) armour. This enhanced protection substantially increased the vehicle's weight to 25 tonnes (24.6 tons), which led to a reduction in the vehicle's top road speed to a modest 38kph (21mph). Minor modifications included external air filters, steel return rollers, a new cupola with a single-piece hatch and thicker armour, and a mount on it for an anti-aircraft machine gun, a new idler, and the omission of side vision ports for the driver and radio operator.

From 1943, Panzer regiments in the Panzer divisions were to have one battalion equipped with Model H and one with Panthers. The Model H became the single most numerous Panzer IV variant and, under Guderian's encouragement, Panzer IV production leapt to 3073 tanks during 1943 and 3161 in 1944–45.

The Final Panzer – Model J

By mid-1944, two major Panzer IV producers – Krupp and Vomag – had switched to manufacturing other vehicles and thus the final Panzer IV variant, the Model J, was built

ABOVE *The Panzer IV Model G sported a redesigned muzzle brake and deleted the vision slits in the turret. Later versions of the Model G added smoke dischargers on the turret sides as a defensive measure, and the very late model had a new type of drive sprocket.*

exclusively by Nibelungenwerke in Austria. This variant, which entered service in March 1944, incorporated many minor modifications, including the increasing replacement of hull side skirts with wire mesh panels. The latter were cheaper and faster to produce, easier to replace and just as effective as metal skirts at deflecting hollow-charge rounds. The suspension of the Model J was also slightly modified from the summer of 1944 to allow the fitting in the field of the new, wider Eastern Track (Ostkette) for winter combat in ice and snow. This wider track was also subsequently retro-fitted to many older Panzer IV tanks.

Growing raw material shortages also led to the abandonment of electrical traverse for the turret and its replacement with a manually operated system that significantly slowed the turret's rate of traverse. However, the redesign of the hull and the removal of the electrical traverse system allowed the fuel capacity of the Model J to be increased to 680 litres (150 gallons), which raised its operational range to an impressive 322km (200 miles) by road and 210km (131 miles) cross-country.

The German High Command had planned to end Panzer IV production in February 1945. In reality, however, the vehicle continued to be built until the end of the war as completion rates had plummeted. This collapse in production was caused both by Allied air attacks on German factories and by mounting raw material shortages. In total, Nibelungenwerke completed 2392 Panzer IV Model J tanks during 1944–45.

Specialised Variants

The Germans built small numbers of various specialised versions of the Panzer IV tank. During early 1940, German factories constructed 20 Panzer IV Model C and D bridge-laying tanks. At the same time the Germans waterproofed 40 Panzer IV tanks for underwater operations in preparation for the projected invasion of Britain. When Hitler cancelled the operation, the Germans utilised these vehicles to storm the Bug River in June 1941 at the start of Operation 'Barbarossa'. German firms also constructed 11 Munitionspanzer IV Karl vehicles during 1941 as munitions carriers, each designed to carry four of the huge 2.2-tonne (2.16-ton) shells for the super-heavy Karl 600mm (23.6in) tracked mortar.

During 1944, the Germans produced 97 Panzer IV command tanks with dummy guns, 90 armoured artillery observation vehicles that retained their main armaments,

ABOVE *A military band performs next to a Panzer IV tank during a ceremony involving troops of the 5th SS Panzer Division* Wiking *in the Soviet Union in November 1943. Note the long-barrelled 7.5cm gun and the large Schürzen side skirting to protect the tracks from hollow-charge rounds.*

and 36 turretless Panzer IV recovery vehicles. Moreover, the stability and the reliability of the Panzer IV chassis meant that it could be used reliably as a platform for a variety of other armoured fighting vehicles, including the Jagdpanzer IV tank destroyer, the StuG IV assault gun, and the Sturmpanzer IV Brummbär (Grizzly Bear) self-propelled heavy assault vehicle.

Anti-aircraft Artillery Tanks

A more significant innovation was the utilisation of the Panzer IV chassis as the basis of several anti-aircraft artillery tanks, or Flakpanzers. Growing Allied air superiority on all fronts from 1943 increased the urgent need for fully tracked mobile anti-aircraft weapons, to replace the existing improvised anti-aircraft vehicles based on artillery tractors and half-tracks.

In September 1943, at Guderian's insistence, Hitler finally authorised construction of a purpose-built Flakpanzer IV anti-aircraft tank that carried a 3.7cm Flak 43 gun in a light armoured shield on the basic Panzer IV chassis. The vehicle had all-round traverse, a seven-man crew, and an ammunition stowage capacity of 416 rounds. The high box-like silhouette led crews to dub the vehicle the Möbelwagen (Furniture Van). This vehicle served throughout 1944 in the self-propelled, anti-aircraft artillery platoons of panzer regiments.

The unsatisfactory armoured protection of this vehicle, however, prompted the Germans to introduce the fundamentally redesigned Flakpanzer IV Wirbelwind (Whirlwind) in December 1943. This vehicle mounted quadruple 2cm anti-aircraft guns in a lightly armoured, 16mm- (0.6in-) thick, open-topped revolving barbette mounted on the standard Panzer IV chassis. The firm of

Ostbau in Silesia produced the vehicle, which proved popular with its crews because it provided them with adequate protection.

With a combat weight of 22.4 tonnes (22 tons), the Whirlwind carried a five-man crew and 3200 rounds of 2cm ammunition. During 1944, three or four of these vehicles were deployed with the headquarters companies of select panzer battalions. Though the vehicle carried sufficient ammunition for 40 minutes of continuous fire, the turret possessed a relatively slow rate of traverse, which was to prove a significant handicap when the vehicle was engaged in combat with its primary target – low-flying ground-attack

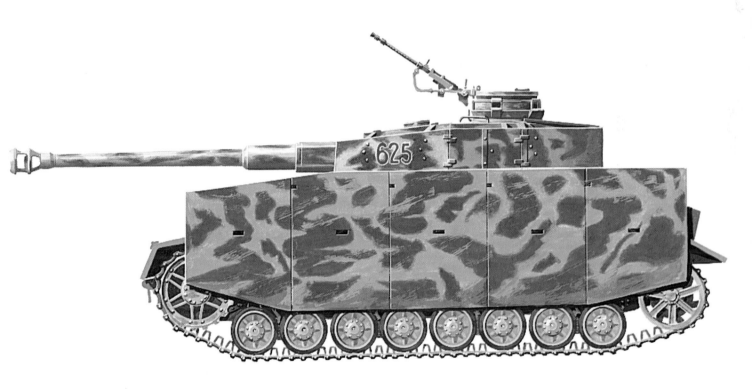

SPECIFICATIONS: Panzer IV Model H (Sdkfz162/1)

GENERAL
Vehicle Type: medium/heavy tank
Entered Service: spring 1943
Crew: four
Combat Weight: 25 tonnes (24.6 tons)

DIMENSIONS
Overall Length: 7.02m (23ft)
Hull Length: 5.90m (19ft 4in)
Width: 3.33m (10ft 11in)
Height: 2.68m (8ft 11in)

ARMAMENT
Main: 7.5cm (3in) KwK 40 L/48 gun

Secondary: 1 x 7.92mm (0.312in) MG 34 in hull front

AMMUNITION
Main: 87 rounds
Secondary: 3150 rounds

ARMOUR
Hull Front: 80mm (3.2in) (at 80 degrees)
Hull Sides: 30mm (1.2in) (at 90 degrees)
Hull Rear: 20mm (0.8in) (at 78 degrees)
Turret Front: 50mm (2in) (at 79 degrees)
Turret Sides: 30mm (1.2in) (at 64 degrees)
Turret Rear: 30mm (1.2in) (at 74 degrees)
Turret Roof: 10mm (0.4in) (at 74 degrees)

MOTIVE POWER
Engine: Maybach HL 120 TRM petrol V12-cylinder petrol
Power: 300 bhp
Fuel Capacity: 470 litres (103 gallons)

PERFORMANCE
Maximum Speed (Road): 38kph (21mph)
Maximum Speed (Cross-Country): 16kph (10mph)
Operational Range (Road): 210km (131 miles)
Operational Range (Cross-Country): 130km (81 miles)

aircraft. Nonetheless, the vehicle proved unexpectedly useful in a secondary ground role, with its 800rpm rate of fire providing formidable defensive firepower against enemy infantry. Ostbau completed just 140 Wirbelwind vehicles before the war ended, too few for it to make any significant tactical impact against the Allies, either in the air or on the ground.

From March 1944, the Flakpanzer IV (3.7cm) Ostwind (East Wind) entered production. The Ostwind proved a successful replacement for the Wirbelwind with its more effective gun. Constructed by Deutsche Eisenwerke, who completed just 40 vehicles, the Ostwind mounted a single 3.7cm Flak 43 anti-aircraft gun capable of 160rpm in a more strongly armoured, rotating turret with 25mm- (1in-) thick plate. The combat weight of the vehicle including its seven-man crew and 4216 rounds of ammunition was 25.4 tonnes (25 tons).

All of these vehicles were expedient designs, however, and their open-topped turrets were a significant tactical drawback, especially when employed in a ground role. Moreover, these vehicles proved only minimally capable of

mitigating local enemy air superiority. The final stage of Flakpanzer IV development was a sophisticated Daimler-Benz design, the Flakpanzer IV Kugelblitz (Ball-Lightning). A purpose-built anti-aircraft tank, the vehicle mounted two 3cm Rheinmetall-Borsig 103/38 modified aircraft cannon in an armoured, revolving, fully enclosed turret. With 360 degree traverse in just 25 seconds and an extraordinary potential rate of fire of 900 rpm, the Kugelblitz was a formidable defensive weapon in both anti-aircraft and ground roles. Its main drawback was its limited ammunition stowage of 1200 rounds, which restricted its tactical effectiveness.

Fortunately for the Allies, their forces overran the Deutsche Eisenwerke factory in the Ruhr after only five vehicles had been completed. Had the Kugelblitz entered German service in large numbers, it would have both

BELOW *Crews of the 1st SS Panzer Division* Leibstandarte *undergo familiarisation training with their new Panzer IV tanks in France during July 1942. The Leibstandarte has redeployed from the Eastern Front for reorganisation and re-equipment in the West.*

powerfully reinforced German defensive capabilities against Allied ground attack aircraft, and mitigated the extent to which overwhelming Allied aerial supremacy hampered German operations during 1944–45.

The Panzer IV in Combat

Throughout the war, German factories produced 10,500 vehicles on the Panzer IV chassis, including more than 7000 tanks. From 1939 to mid-1944, the Panzer IV could generally hold its own against any opponent, with the main exception when it was in combat on the Eastern Front in late 1941 and early 1942 – before up-gunning and up-armouring had taken place. Even during 1944, though, the Panzer IV remained the mainstay of the German defence on all fronts and typically equipped one battalion in each panzer division, the other fielding Panther tanks. The SS Kampfgruppe Peiper, the spearhead of the German Ardennes counter-offensive, for example, was able to field an equal mix of Panzer IV and Panther tanks.

Strengths and Weaknesses

By mid-1944, however, the Panzer IV was becoming outclassed: first, the tank's poorly sloped armour was increasingly inadequate against heavier Allied anti-tank and tank guns and loss rates were consequently high; second, the performance of the Panzer IV's gun increasingly compared unfavourably with that of newer German and enemy armoured fighting vehicles; lastly, the tank's speed was unimpressive for a vehicle of that size and weight. Yet the high quality training and skilled gunnery of German armoured crews, as well as realistic German doctrine and tactics ensured that in the last year of the war the Panzer IV could still often hold its own against enemy armour in situations of near numerical parity.

The Panzer IV not only proved very robust and mechanically reliable, which contributed to high serviceability rates, but also possessed a good operational range, especially the Model J. The tank's greatest strength was its capacity for modernisation and improvement, which ensured that it remained in German service throughout World War II. This quality allowed the Germans to keep producing an effective combat tank until the third generation of German medium and heavy tanks – the Panther and Tiger – could enter service and counter the new Soviet heavy armour. Although less famous than the better known tanks that succeeded it, the Panzer IV remained the backbone of the German panzer force throughout the war.

CHAPTER II

JAGDPANZER IV

**Following its standard practice, the German Army produced
a limited traverse tank destroyer version of the Panzer IV,
which ultimately mounted the powerful long-barrelled
7.5cm gun carried by the Panzer V Panther tank.
The Jagdpanzer IV fought in Italy and Normandy in 1944,
as well as on the Eastern Front.**

In August 1944, Hitler ordered that German firms entirely abandon Panzer IV tank production by the end of the year, to concentrate instead on construction of its tank destroyer derivative, the Jagdpanzer IV which had entered production in January 1944. The design originated from a late 1942 request for a new tank-destroyer with no less than 100mm (3.9in) frontal armour, based on the standard Panzer IV chassis. The Army Weapons Department intended that this vehicle should carry the superb long-barrelled 7.5cm L/70 gun of the Panther tank in a limited-traverse mounting, housed in a low-silhouetted armoured superstructure. In reality, however, three different versions of this vehicle appeared, only two of which mounted this Panther gun.

LEFT *The Panzer IV/70 (V) variant of the Jagdpanzer IV finally mounted the long-barrelled 7.5cm L/70 Panther gun for which it was originally intended. Note the folded-down gun cradle on the hull front used to support the long barrel when the vehicle travelled long distances by road.*

The Army Weapons Department conceived the Jagdpanzer IV tank destroyer as an improved version of the StuG III assault gun, which it would eventually replace. Heinz Guderian, the Inspector-General of Armoured Forces, however, was against the project from the start. He was entirely satisfied with the development potential of the StuG III and did not wish to divert any of the production capacity currently devoted to the Panzer IV tank, then the mainstay of the German armoured force. The Jagdpanzer IV soon gained the pejorative nickname of 'Guderian's Duck' as a result of his outspoken opposition to the project. This disagreement ensured that the development of the vehicle fell behind intended schedules.

Development History

A full-sized mockup of the Jagdpanzer IV was not shown to Hitler until September 1943, and the firm of Vomag only began constructing a few pre-production vehicles by the end of that year. The project, however, was dogged by significant production difficulties, particularly in modifying the long-barrelled 70-calibre gun of the Panther tank to fit within a new well-sloped and armoured superstructure. During this period, the German Army desperately needed to deliver large numbers of armoured fighting vehicles to the frontline troops. Given this requirement, the delay in development of the 7.5cm L/70-equipped Jagdpanzer IV led to the construction of an interim assault gun on the Panzer IV chassis, the Sturmgeschütz IV (Sdkfz 163). This vehicle married a modified version of the standard StuG III superstructure and its 7.5cm L/48 gun directly onto the chassis of the Panzer IV tank. Between December 1943 and March 1945, German firms constructed 1139 StuG IV vehicles, which saw service alongside the StuG III with both assault gun and anti-tank units.

L/48-gunned Variants

Since modification of the 7.5cm L/70 Panther gun for the Jagdpanzer IV continued to suffer unexpected and exasperating delays right through to early 1944, the High Command requested that Vomag commence production of the Jagdpanzer IV utilising available stocks of the 7.5cm KwK 40 L/48 gun, as fitted in the StuG III and Panzer IV. This L/48-gunned tank destroyer first entered service in January 1944 and was designated simply as the Jagdpanzer IV (Sdkfz 162). The vehicle possessed an excellent level of protection thanks to its well-sloped armour that maximised shot deflection. Its upper and lower frontal nose plates, for example, were sloped at 45 and 57 degrees, respectively. The vehicle carried 60mm (2.4in) of frontal armour and 30mm- (1.2in-) thick plate on its superstructure sides. The vehicle's rear superstructure sides also possessed additional 5mm- (0.2in-) spaced appliqué plates welded on top of the basic armour, and the vehicle carried Schürzen side skirts against hollow-charge rounds. All external surfaces were covered with Zimmerit anti-magnetic mine paste before leaving the factory.

The 75mm L/48 gun of the Jagdpanzer IV was mounted offset 200mm (8in) to the right of the centre line in a sloping front plate set in a squat, sloped, all-welded superstructure. Early vehicles also possessed a muzzle brake on the main armament. However, as the vehicle had such a low silhouette – the barrel was only 1.4m (4ft 7in) above the ground when horizontal – the muzzle brake threw up dust from the deflected blast when the gun fired. This heavy back-blast obstructed the crew's vision and could give away the vehicle's position to the enemy. As a result, later vehicles had the muzzle brake deleted. The vehicle weighed

24.1 tonnes (23.7 tons) and was powered by the standard 300bhp Maybach HL 120 TRM engine used in the Panzer IV tank. German firms produced 769 Jagdpanzer IV (Sdkfz 162) vehicles between January and November 1944 at an average rate of 70 units per month.

L/70-gunned Variants

Eventually, later production models of the Jagdpanzer IV received a modified version of the longer 7.5cm L/70 Panther gun originally intended for the vehicle. The Germans designated this up-gunned Jagdpanzer IV variant as the Panzerjäger IV für 7.5cm StuK 42 L/70 (Sdkfz 162/1). This vehicle, however, was more commonly (if erroneously) called the Panzer IV/70 or IV/70(V), wrongly implying that it was a tank rather than a tank destroyer.

The first L/70-equipped Jagdpanzer IV vehicles joined combat in small numbers during August 1944. The larger gun necessitated some minor changes to the vehicle, particularly to offset the increased weight exerted on the vehicle's nose. The Panzer IV/70(V) possessed interlocking upper and lower hull nose plates, and superstructure front and sides plates, respectively, for added strength. The 80mm- (3.2in-) thick upper hull nose plate was set at an angle of 45 degrees, while the 45mm (1.8in) armour on the lower hull nose sloped at an angle of 55 degrees. The compartment for the five-man crew occupied the front three-quarters of the vehicle and the rear section housed a standard 300bhp Maybach HL 120 TRM engine.

The modified long-barrelled 7.5cm L/70 gun carried by the Panzer IV/70(V) was ballistically identical to the 7.5cm KwK 42 L/70 Panther tank gun. This main armament, which had no muzzle brake, was again located offset 200mm (8in) to the right. The long gun overhung the hull front by 2.58m (8ft 6in), which made the vehicle nose-heavy. In order to fit this gun into the vehicle's shallow superstructure, the gun's buffer and recuperator mechanisms had to be relocated above the barrel; it was this modification which had so delayed early development of the project. The vehicle carried 55 rounds of 7.5cm ammunition and also sported a ball-mounted 7.92mm MG 34 fitted in the hull front for local defence. Both the longer gun and heavier armour increased the vehicle's weight to 25.8 tonnes (25.4 tons). German factories produced 930 Panzer IV/70(V) vehicles between August 1944 and March 1945 at an average rate of 103 vehicles per month.

In early 1945, a very small number of late-production Panzer IV/70(V) vehicles were constructed on the modified hybrid Panzer III/IV chassis, which featured the three return rollers of the Panzer III rather than the four carried on the

Panzer IV. German factories were forced to employ this expedient to maintain the rate of production, thanks to shortages in the availability of the robust Panzer IV chassis. These few vehicles were identical to their predecessor in all other respects, being identifiable only by the reduced number of return rollers on the chassis.

The Final Variant

The final variant of the Jagdpanzer IV was the Panzer IV/70 Zwischenlösung (interim) or IV/70(A). German firms developed this special stopgap version of the Jagdpanzer IV to overcome existing delays and bottlenecks in Panzer IV/70(V) production. The Germans achieved this through

the simple expedient of mounting the 7.5cm StuK 42 L/70 gun, and a modified version of the IV/70(V) superstructure, directly on top of the unmodified standard chassis of the Panzer IV Model J tank. This chassis was at the time in mass production and thus immediately available in large numbers. This conversion also involved a less complex process that enabled German factories to produce a finished vehicle more rapidly.

Adoption of the new chassis, however, necessitated some modification of the existing IV/70(V) superstructure, which was carried out by Alkett. These modifications meant that the interim Panzer IV/70(A) vehicle was easily distinguishable from its sister model, the Panzer IV/70(V), in

SPECIFICATIONS: Jagdpanzer IV (Panzer IV/70V) (Sdkfz 162/1)

GENERAL
Vehicle Type: tank destroyer
(self-propelled anti-tank gun)
Entered Service: summer 1944
Crew: five
Combat Weight: 25.8 tonnes
(25.4 tons)
Chassis: Panzer IV

DIMENSIONS
Overall Length: 8.60m (28ft 2in)
Hull Length: 6.04m (19ft 10in)
Width: 3.28m (10 ft 5in)
Height: 1.96m (6ft 5in)

ARMAMENT
Main: 7.5cm (3in) StuK 42 L/70 gun
Main Gun Traverse: 10 degrees left to
10 degrees right

Secondary: 1 x 7.92mm (0.312in) MG 34
in hull front

AMMUNITION STOWAGE
Main: 55 rounds
Secondary: 600 rounds

ARMOUR
Hull Front: 80mm (3.2in) (at 50 degrees)
Hull Front (Driver's Plate): 80mm
(3.2in) (at 45 degrees)
Hull Sides: 30mm (1.2in) (at 90 degrees)
Hull Rear: 20mm (0.8in) (at 60 degrees)
Superstructure Front: 80mm (3.2in)
(at 45 degrees)
Superstructure Sides: 40mm (1.6in)
(at 60 degrees)
Superstructure Rear: 30mm (1.2in)
(at 78 degrees)

Superstructure Roof: 20mm (0.8in)
(at 0 degrees)

MOTIVE POWER
Engine: Maybach HL 120 TRM V12-
cylinder petrol
Power: 300 bhp
Fuel Capacity: 470 litres
(103 gallons)

PERFORMANCE
Maximum Speed (Road): 45kph
(28mph)
Maximum Speed (Cross-Country):
24kph (15 mph)
Operational Range (Road): 210km
(130 miles)
Operational Range (Cross-Country):
130km (80 miles)

that it lacked the latter's sloped rear superstructure. Instead the IV/70(A) possessed a cut-back rear superstructure and a vertical rear plate, which from a distance ensured that it was often mistaken for a tank. At 28 tonnes (27.6 tons), the weight of this interim variant was rather more than its sister vehicle. The IV/70(A) also possessed a standard of protection similar to that of its predecessor. The tank destroyer had 85mm- (3.3in-) thick armour on the hull nose and driver's plate, 30mm (1.2in) side and rear armour, and an impressive 120mm (4.7in) on the gun mantlet. The vehicle had a maximum speed of 38kph (24mph) and

BELOW *This Jagdpanzer IV mounted the 7.5cm L/48 gun in a long low-silhouetted superstructure. What makes this 1944 picture so unusual is the presence of an Elefant tank destroyer in the background – a very rare vehicle at this stage of the war. Both have been captured by the Western Allies.*

an operational range of 322km (200 miles). The Nibelungenwerke factory in Austria produced 278 Panzer IV/70(A) vehicles between August 1944 and March 1945 at an average rate of 34 units per month.

Performance of the Jagdpanzer IV

With a low silhouette, well-sloped armour, good mobility and lethal firepower – especially the later vehicles armed with the 7.5cm StuK 42 L/70 gun – the Jagdpanzer IV was a very efficient design as a tank destroyer. However, the extra weight of the long gun made the tank very nose-heavy so much so that the front road wheels had to be ringed with steel instead of rubber to deal with the extra weight. The extra weight also affected the tank's performance, especially over rough terrain. (By the later stages of the war such drawbacks simply had to be overlooked, as the Allies were

ABOVE *As can be seen from this picture, the Jagdpanzer IV chassis had the same basic hull suspension and drive train as the Panzer IV chassis from which it was designed. The superstructure itself was built from sloping plates.*

closing in on the Germans and anything that could be put in the field was used.)

After entering production in January 1944, the Jagdpanzer IV gradually replaced the Marder II and Marder III self-propelled anti-tank guns in the tank destroyer battalions of panzer divisions. It remained a relatively uncommon vehicle, though, and despite ambitious production schedules only 1977 vehicles of all three types were completed. Consequently, the vehicle remained a rare machine during 1944. For example, it partially equipped just six of the 10 mechanised divisions in the West on 6 June 1944, and then only in sufficient quantities to equip a single company in each of these division's individual tank destroyer battalions. Consequently, no more than 60 Jagdpanzer IV vehicles fought in the Normandy campaign. The three Jagdpanzer IV variants, however, became more numerous in the last six months of the war as production mounted. An incomplete tank inventory of the German Army, on 1 April 1945, recorded that 275 Jagdpanzer IV tank destroyers armed with the long 7.5cm gun (that is, both Panzer IV/70 vehicles) were still in operational service.

The Jagdpanzer IV tank destroyer's powerful armament made it a formidable defensive weapon, particularly in the West against less well-armoured Anglo-American tanks, but like all German armoured fighting vehicles, the Jagdpanzer IV was not produced in sufficient numbers to have a significant tactical impact.

JAGDPANZER 38(t) HETZER

The Hetzer was a completely new design using the well-proven components of the Panzer 38(t). Though it had a cramped fighting compartment and a limited angle of fire, which presented problems in battle, it proved itself a capable tank destroyer, and after the war served with the Czech and Swiss armies.

During 1942–43, in response to the threat posed by Soviet medium T34 and heavy KV1 tanks, Germany produced a series of improvised light tank destroyers by marrying powerful anti-tank guns to obsolete tank chassis to create the Marder (Marten) series of vehicles. Although these tanks were reasonably successful in the field, the overall results of such a conversion were tall and cumbersome vehicles that were without style and clearly demonstrated the drawbacks of hasty production. The German Army quickly realised that even though the Marder series provided much-needed mobile anti-tank firepower they were, after all, only interim vehicles. Another solution was needed.

LEFT The Hetzer was produced in response to Colonel-General Heinz Guderian's demand for a light tank destroyer to replace existing light self-propelled guns and towed howitzers. Production commenced in April 1944.

In contrast to the Marder, the Germans had recognised at the same time that the various Sturmgeschütz close-support artillery vehicles could also be used as tank destroyers. The Germans realised that the advantages of the two tanks could possibly be married together. Thus, it was the success achieved in the anti-tank role by the Sturmgeschütz (StuG) III self-propelled assault gun, which mounted a 7.5cm gun in a fully enclosed and well-armoured superstructure, that finally pointed the way for future German tank destroyer development.

Development History

During 1943, the Army Weapons Department chose the reliable Czech Panzer 38(t) chassis as the platform for a purpose-built light tank destroyer to replace the Marder vehicles then in service in the anti-tank battalions of infantry divisions. The result was one of the finest of the Panzerjägers – the Jagdpanzer 38(t) für 7.5cm Pak 39 (L/48), or the

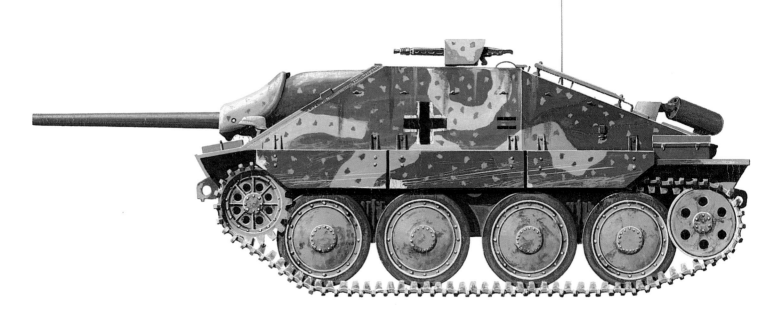

SPECIFICATIONS: Jagdpanzer 38(t) Hetzer

GENERAL
Vehicle Type: light tank destroyer
(self-propelled anti-tank gun)
Entered Service: spring 1944
Crew: four
Combat Weight: 16 tonnes
(15.7 tons)
Chassis: Panzer 38(t)

DIMENSIONS
Overall Length: 6.27m (20ft 7in)
Hull Length: 4.87m (15ft 11in)
Width: 2.63m (8ft 7in)
Height: 2.1m (6ft 10in)

ARMAMENT
Main: 7.5cm (3in) Pak 39 L/48 gun
Main Gun Traverse: 11 degrees left to
5 degrees right

Secondary: 1 x 7.92mm (0.312in) MG 34,
roof-mounted

AMMUNITION STOWAGE
Main: 41 rounds
Secondary: 780 rounds

ARMOUR
Hull Front (Nose): 60mm (2.4in)
(at 40 degrees)
Hull Front (Driver's Plate): 60mm
(2.4in) (at 30 degrees)
Hull Sides: 20mm (0.8in) (at 60 degrees)
Hull Rear: 8mm (0.3in) (at 70 degrees)
Superstructure Front: 60mm (2.4in)
(at 30 degrees)
Superstructure Sides: 20mm (0.8in)
(at 75 degrees)
Superstructure Rear: 20mm (0.8in)

(at 75 degrees)
Superstructure Roof: 8mm (0.3in)
(at 0 degrees)

MOTIVE POWER
Engine: (Czech) Praga EPA TZJ R6-cylinder
petrol
Power: 158 bhp
Fuel Capacity: 386 litres (85 gallons)

PERFORMANCE
Maximum Speed (Road): 26kph
(16mph)
Maximum Speed (Cross-Country):
15kph (9mph)
Operational Range (Road): 161kms
(100 miles)
Operational Range (Cross-Country)
80kms (50 miles)

Jagdpanzer 38(t) Hetzer (Baiter), as it was more commonly known.

The Hetzer proved to be one of the most advanced tank destroyers to be built during World War II. The vehicle, which weighed only 16 tonnes (15.7 tons), emerged in prototype form in 1943 and went into production during the spring of 1944. The first Hetzer vehicles entered service with infantry anti-tank battalions during May 1944 and by 1945 the Hetzer had become the most numerous tank destroyer in German service. At first only BMM constructed the vehicle, but from September 1944 Skoda joined the production programme. German firms completed a total of 2804 Hetzer chassis before the end of the war, including

2584 Jagdpanzer 38(t) vehicles. Of these 2584 Hetzers, some 2496 were issued to combat units, including 100 that the Germans supplied to the Hungarian Army.

The Hetzer mounted a modified version of the 48-calibre long 7.5cm Pak 39 L/48 gun already installed in the Panzer IV tank. The gun possessed an improved recoil mechanism that dispensed with the need for a muzzle brake. It was fitted in a limited traverse mount in the front of a steeply sloped, low-silhouetted armoured superstructure on a specially modified Panzer 38(t) chassis, which had been widened to accommodate the size of the gun. The Hetzer also possessed specially widened and reinforced tracks to take the added weight of the vehicle, brought about by both its larger gun and enhanced armour. The Hetzer's protection consisted of 60mm- (2.4in-) thick plate sloped at 40–60 degrees on the hull nose, just 8mm (0.3in) roof and rear armour and 20mm (0.8in) plate set at 20 degrees on the superstructure sides. In addition, the gun mantlet was protected by 30mm (1.2in) armour and production models also carried 5mm- (0.2in-) thick side apron plates (Schürzen) to ward off hollow-charge rounds.

The small size of the Hetzer ensured that the gun barrel considerably overhung the front of the vehicle. The main armament was mounted 380mm (15in) off the centre line to the right, in a distinctive Saukopf (Pig's Head) mantlet, designed to minimise the possibility of deflection of incoming rounds down into the hull. The elevation of the gun was restricted to only 16 degrees overall (from -6 to +10 degrees), as was the horizontal traverse which ranged from 11 degrees left to 5 degrees right. As secondary armament, the Hetzer mounted a remotely controlled 7.92mm MG 34 machine gun on the superstructure top, operated by the commander via a periscope and an extended trigger from inside the vehicle. This weapon, which was capable of 360 degree rotation, provided local defence against enemy infantry. The small size of the vehicle limited ammunition stowage to only 41 rounds for the main armament and 780 rounds for the machine gun.

The suspension of the Jagdpanzer 38(t) consisted of four large running wheels on either side for maximum speed. The standard 150bhp Czech Praga EPA R6-cylinder petrol engine used in the Panzer 38(t) tank also powered the Hetzer. But the heavier weight of the vehicle reduced its power-to-weight ratio to just 9.4 bhp per tonne (9.6 bhp/ton), which restricted the Hetzer's top speed to a relatively slow 26kph (16mph) by road and a sluggish 15kph (9mph) cross-country. The Hetzer mounted two fuel tanks with a total capacity of 386 litres (85 gallons), which gave the vehicle an operational range of approximately 161km (100 miles) by road and 80km (50 miles) cross-country.

The Hetzer in Combat

During 1944, the Hetzer joined the self-propelled anti-tank companies of infantry divisions and progressively replaced both the remaining Marder vehicles still in service, as well as StuG III assault guns filling in for lack of suitable purpose-built tank destroyers. The German infantry division organisation of 1944 authorised 10 Hetzer tank destroyers, but production delays and mounting combat losses ensured that this goal was rarely attained. During the spring of 1945 the German Army introduced a new 1945-pattern infantry

division whose redesignated tank destroyer company theoretically possessed 14 Hetzers, though again a wide gap existed between paper establishments and reality. In fact, only one-quarter of the approximately 100 German infantry divisions still in existence in April 1945 had received any Hetzers, let alone a full allotment. None of the German infantry divisions isolated in Norway, nor in the Courland pocket, in Estonia, for example, ever received Hetzers. Thus, in German infantry service, the Jagdpanzer 38(t) never entirely replaced the StuG III, or the various Marder vehicles, numbers of which continued to serve alongside the Hetzer until the end of the war.

In addition to service with the infantry, the Jagdpanzer 38(t) also saw combat with a variety of other German units. The Hetzer served in the anti-tank battalions of four panzer divisions (the 2nd and 10th SS and the army 8th and 16th) as well as in those of three panzergrenadier divisions (18th, 25th, and Kurmark). The vehicle also equipped five assault gun brigades and seven independent army tank destroyer battalions. Lastly, two independent companies attached to the V SS Mountain Corps, together with the escort battalion of the head of the SS, Reichsführer Heinrich Himmler, employed Hetzer tank destroyers. The incomplete German inventory of 1 April 1945 reveals that at least 627 Hetzers remained in service with all these various units, making it the second most numerous German armoured fighting vehicle after the StuG III assault gun.

Production – 1945 onwards

During the last months of the war, the Germans also supplied Hetzers to the Hungarian Army in a futile effort to bolster its disintegrating morale and combat effectiveness. At least one Hungarian Hetzer battalion was formed and deployed on the southern sector of the Eastern Front in Hungary, during the closing stages of the war. The location of the Skoda and BMM works in the German Protectorate of Bohemia-Moravia ensured that the Hetzer was one of the last German armoured fighting vehicles to cease production, and no less than 121 machines were built and issued to combat formations in the last month of the war.

Such was the utility of the design that after May 1945 Skoda both continued to build the Hetzer for the Czech Army. Between 1946 and 1952, the firm also sold 158 vehicles to the Swiss Army, where they remained in service until 1970. Captured Hetzer tank destroyers also continued to see service in the Red Army and Warsaw Pact satellite armies into the 1950s.

The Hetzer proved an economical and efficient light tank destroyer that provided mobile anti-tank firepower in

ABOVE *The Hetzer fulfilled a requirement for a tank destroyer that was adequately armoured, with overhead protection and a low silhouette. It used angled armour extensively, and usually carried a roof-mounted, remote-control machine gun.*

support of German infantry. The Jagdpanzer 38(t) proved a valuable infantry support vehicle thanks to the combination of its fuel economy, small size and low silhouette – the vehicle was just 2.1m (6ft 10in) tall. This was especially true for the defensive fighting that the Germans conducted during the last 18 months of the war.

Significant Drawbacks

Although generally well designed, the Hetzer had a number of significant drawbacks, however, and was not a popular vehicle with its crews. The vehicle's most serious operational limitation was the traverse of its main armament, which at 16 degrees, both vertically and horizontally, was the most restricted of any wartime German tank destroyer. Its limited traverse meant that the entire vehicle had to be slewed to cover a target moving

across the front, thus exposing the vehicle's more thinly armoured sides to the enemy. The layout of the four-man crew was also poor with the gunner and loader both positioned on the left hand side of the main armament, in a vehicle designed for right-handed operation. It was thus difficult for the loader to reach the ammunition supply on the right of the vehicle, and this factor reduced the Hetzer's rate of fire. The commander was also remote in the right rear of the vehicle, with poor means of communication and observation and it was thus difficult for him to coordinate with the gunner and driver in order to engage and destroy targets.

Overall, therefore, although the Hetzer packed a great deal – including a heavy punch and good armoured protection - on a small chassis, it suffered from the inevitable trade-offs of such an arrangement, in terms of lack of power and speed as well as poor cross-country performance. Nonetheless, the Hetzer was a distinct improvement on the improvised Marder series of vehicles, especially in terms of armour protection, and its small size and low silhouette partially compensated for its other deficiencies. As a cheap,

352d Company lost six of its 10 vehicles in its first engagement. All the remaining Flammpanzer 38(t) vehicles were destroyed between January and March 1945.

Bergepanzer 38(t)

Another uncommon variant was the Bergefahrzeuge 38(t) Hetzer recovery vehicle, or Bergepanzer 38(t) as it was more commonly called. German factories constructed 170 such vehicles, including 64 converted directly from battle-damaged Hetzers. The Bergepanzer 38(t) lacked the superstructure of the original vehicle and carried instead a low wooden box shield that provided minimal protection for the four-man crew. The vehicle mounted a winch in place of the main armament and weighed 14.5 tonnes (14.2 tons). Unfortunately, the Bergepanzer 38(t) did not prove a success because the vehicle's engine was simply too weak to pull the heavy tanks and tank destroyers that dominated the German armoured fighting vehicle inventory by 1945.

The Bison

Finally, German factories constructed 30 vehicles designated the Bison – a 15cm Heavy Infantry Gun 33 on the self-propelled 38(t) chassis. These were identical to the Bison 15cm self-propelled infantry guns produced on the Panzer 38(t) chassis, except that these were constructed utilising the modified Jagdpanzer 38(t) Hetzer chassis. Of these 30 vehicles, six were converted from battle-damaged Hetzer tank destroyers. This Bison variant weighed 16.5 tonnes (16.2 tons) and served with the self-propelled heavy infantry gun companies of select panzergrenadier regiments.

Jagdpanzer 38(t) Starr

The initial decision to proceed with the production of the Jagdpanzer 38(t) Hetzer in December 1943 was in fact taken on the basis that it would be built with a rigid, mounted gun. Indeed, both Rheinmetall and Alkett had proved the feasibility of such an idea, the latter mounting a rigid 7.5cm Pak39 in the Jagdpanzer IV, in a mounting for the 38(t). The first of 10 units was delivered in mid-1944. But technical problems with the hand wheels and the sights meant that production of this vehicle could only be continued with the addition of the recoiling 7.5cm Pak39 instead. By the end of the year the problems with the rigid mount had still not been resolved, and production of the normal Hetzer continued.

Nevertheless, the Starr's stronger front plate and reduced overall weight were advantages over the Hetzer, which meant that it was kept in development. However, the war ended before a decision on full production could be made.

easily produced and fuel efficient vehicle, the Hetzer was well-suited to the defensive warfare in which the Germans found themselves predominantly engaged during the last 18 months of the war.

Flammpanzer 38(t)

Small numbers of three specialised vehicles were constructed on the basic Hetzer chassis. German firms constructed 20 flame thrower variants of the Hetzer, known as the Flammpanzer 38(t), which served with the 352nd and 353rd Flame Tank Companies. Hitler intended that these vehicles be first used in the German Ardennes counter-offensive in the West, but they were not ready in time. Instead, the two companies made their operational debut in Operation 'Nordwind' (north wind), the German offensive in Alsace of January 1945. The Flammpanzer 38(t) mounted a flame thrower in place of the main armament, with a dummy barrel fixed over the flame gun to disguise its true function. The vehicle carried 700 litres (154 gallons) of fuel for the flame thrower, which had a range of 60m (197ft). The vehicles did not prove a great success, however, and the

CHAPTER 13

PANZER V PANTHER

The Panther was probably the best tank of World War II, in that it combined nicely the potent 7.5cm gun with excellent sloped armour and reasonable battlefield mobility. The German Army came to rely increasingly on the Panzer V and by the last year of the war it formed the mainstay of Germany's depleted armoured forces.

At the time of Operation 'Barbarossa', the Soviet T34 tank combined mobility, firepower and protection into an excellent combat vehicle that was superior to any German tank then in service. The T34 tank clearly demonstrated this superiority on 4 October 1941, when it badly mauled the 4th Panzer Division at Mtsensk, near Orel. General Guderian – the creator of the German tank arm – commanded the Second Panzer Army to which the 4th Panzer Division belonged and he urgently requested, and was granted, an inquiry into the character of armoured warfare on the Eastern Front. In its initial report of 25 November 1941, this investigating commission ascribed the superiority of the T34 to three design features absent in

LEFT *An early production Panzer Model D drives through a wood during a German counter-attack against Red Army units in the autumn of 1943. This version is distinguishable from its successor variant by its lack of a machine gun in the well-shaped hull frontal plate.*

existing German tanks: sloped all-round armour for optimum shot-deflection; large road wheels and wide tracks for speed, mobility and stability; and a long, overhanging, large-calibre gun that produced a high muzzle velocity and thus good penetration. Before these first encounters with the T34, Germany had pursued heavy tank projects with indifference. After 1935, the Germans had leisurely sought to develop a heavy tank prototype, but the first such vehicle – the VK3001 (DB) – was not completed until 1938. In that same year Henschel also produced a prototype for a 30-tonne (29.5-ton) heavy breakthrough tank, designated the Durchwagen 1 (DW1).

Development History

This design abandoned the standard arrangement of small-diameter bogie wheels and return rollers, used on existing German tanks, for interleaved large-diameter bogie wheels that increased both vehicle speed and wheel life. The

potential of the DW1 vehicle led Henschel to develop a larger 35-tonne (34.4-ton) prototype, the DW2. This tank was equipped with a 300bhp Maybach petrol engine and mounted the short-barrelled 7.5cm L/24 gun then being installed in the Panzer IV tank. All told, Henschel completed eight DW2 prototypes during 1940.

Features of all three of these vehicles – the VK3001, DW1 and DW2 – were incorporated into the official Army Weapons Department contract of January 1942, issued to MAN and Daimler-Benz, to design a 30-tonne (29.5-ton) VK3002 prototype. The design specification included the stipulations made by the Panzer Commission on 25 November 1941, that any new medium tank design should incorporate the sloped all-round armour, the large road wheels and wide tracks, as well as the overhanging gun of the T34 tank. The VK3002 (DB) prototype closely resembled the T34 in design, but the Panther Commission, as the investigating commission had now become known, chose the more conventional VK3002 (MAN) prototype. Powered by a 650bhp Maybach HL 210 engine, the vehicle had sloped armour and interleaved wheels with torsion bar suspension. The design had the turret situated well back to mount a new envisaged longer-barrelled (70-calibres long) 7.5cm gun. During its development, the VK3002 (MAN) prototype unofficially became known as the Panther – after the commission responsible for its genesis –

ABOVE *A rear view of a mid-production Panther Model A. Note the six Schürzen side skirting plates, the twin exhausts at the rear and the prominent commander's cupola, which is located well to the rear of the turret.*

and the title stuck. In May 1942, the Army Weapons Department selected the MAN vehicle for production and during the summer the Germans devoted considerable energies to establishing production facilities. However, overhasty design and production meant that the finished pre-production vehicles weighed 43 tonnes (42.3 tons), well above the target weight limit of 35 tonnes (34.4 tons). This excessive weight caused numerous mechanical problems in the Panther – excessive strain of the gearbox and transmission especially – which the Germans never entirely solved.

To cope with these problems, which became apparent in field trials of the pre-production prototypes, the Germans installed a more powerful 700bhp Maybach HL 230 engine and a more durable AK 7-200 gearbox in the first production model, designated the Panzer V Panther Model D (Sdkfz 171). These modifications only partially ameliorated the numerous mechanical problems that dogged early Panther tanks. In November 1942, the Germans commenced mass production of the Model D at the MAN factory. The importance the German High Command placed on the new tank was illustrated by the establishment of an initial output level of 250 vehicles per month, an ambitious goal for a new production model. Yet even this formidable initial target paled in comparison with the projected rate of 600 Panthers per month that Hitler demanded be reached by the spring of 1944. Such goals were beyond the capacity of MAN alone and during the spring of 1943 Daimler-Benz, MNH, and Henschel all commenced general production of the Panther tank. The Panther Model D was operated by a crew of five and possessed 80–110mm- (3.2–4.3in-) thick frontal armour and 40–45mm- (1.6–1.8in-) thick plate on the sides and roof. From February 1944, the Germans retro-fitted most surviving Model D Panthers with welded 5mm (0.2in) skirt plates (Schürzen) along the bottom edge of the superstructure to protect the track tops. The tank's turret was hydraulically powered and its engine was mounted in the rear of the main fighting compartment. In July 1943, Hitler ordered that production of the problematic Model D be terminated, although production delays at Henschel ensured that it only completed its remaining partially finished Model D tanks in September 1943. In total, German factories delivered 600 Model D vehicles, a figure well below projected targets.

Early experience of the Panther Model D revealed deep-rooted mechanical problems which could only be corrected through extensive testing and fundamental modification. In particular, the vehicle's weight caused excessive wear on the suspension and gears and the more powerful 700bhp engine placed enormous strain on the transmission. Despite these manifest deficiencies, the Germans still deployed two Panther-equipped tank battalions to participate in Operation 'Citadel', the German offensive which began on 5 July 1943 and was designed to encircle Soviet forces in the Kursk salient and thus regain the strategic initiative on the Eastern Front. Indeed, Hitler postponed the offensive from May to gain another month's worth of newly produced Panther and Tiger tanks, as well as the new Elefant tank destroyer.

Some 250 Panther Model D tanks participated in Operation 'Citadel' in the 51st and 52nd Panzer Battalions, which were combined into an improvised Panther Brigade. The Model D made an inauspicious operational debut on 5 July, as this

BELOW *A 1943-produced Panther Model D, which lacked a hull machine-gun. Note the width of the tracks and the smoke launchers fitted at the top front of the turret sides. The Model D experienced many problems due to overhurried development.*

variant suffered severe reliability problems in combat due to frequent mechanical breakdowns. Many Panthers also suffered engine fires, brought about by insufficient levels of engine cooling and ventilation, this problem resulting from watertight sealing of the engine compartment to prepare the tank for amphibious wading. Such widespread damage to gears, transmission and suspension prevented the Panther from living up to German expectations. Moreover, operationally, dense Soviet minefields that were not properly cleared inflicted a heavy toll on the Panthers. This combination of mechanical and tactical problems resulted in the 51st Panzer Battalion suffering a disastrous 56 percent loss rate on its first day of action. By the second day of the Kursk offensive just one-fifth of the Panthers which had been committed remained operational.

In the wake of the Kursk offensive, the Armoured Troop Command concluded that the presently configured Panther Model D was unfit for frontline service. As a result, the Germans implemented a series of modifications to the vehicle. These included a new cast cupola, which improved both the commander's protection and field of vision. The lessons of Kursk also led the Germans to introduce an improved Panther Model A vehicle during the late summer of 1944. This vehicle was distinguishable from its predecessor by its ball-mounted bow machine gun which allowed a wider field of fire. Other modifications included strengthened road wheels to counteract the overloading of the suspension.

During the autumn, a series of minor alterations to the tank's transmission and gearbox progressively corrected the earlier mechanical problems. At the same time, introduction of additional cooling pipes and abandonment of watertight sealing reduced the Panther's susceptibility to engine fires, the failing that had crippled so many vehicles at Kursk. Finally, from September 1943, the Germans fitted all new Panthers with Zimmerit anti-magnetic mine paste applied on the hull and turret to hinder the attachment of hollow-charge magnetic anti-tank mines, though the application was abandoned in September 1944 as an unnecessary luxury, since Germany's opponents rarely used magnetic mines. In total, German firms produced 1768 Panther Model A tanks during 1943–44.

In February 1944, a further improved version, the Panther Model G, entered service. This variant incorporated several design features originally designed for the Panther II tank, the next generation medium tank intended to replace the Panther. Delayed development of the Panther II ultimately prompted the Germans to abandon the project and to incorporate most of its advanced features into the Panther Model G. As a result, the new vehicle included a

major redesign of the hull. This modification introduced sloped, rather than vertical, armour plates on the lower-hull sides, upper side-armour thickened from 40mm (1.6in) to 50mm (2in), and more steeply sloped armour. This redesign enhanced armour shot-deflection capabilities, simplified production, and improved use of available space. These alterations allowed main armament stowage to be increased from 79 to 82 rounds.

Joined by the firm of Demag, the consortium of factories building the Panther finally began mass production of the Model G during the spring of 1944 and this variant stayed in production until the end of the war. German firms constructed 3740 Panther Model G tanks during 1944, and

monthly production peaked at 155 units in August of that year. Thereafter, mounting raw material shortages and the effects of Allied air attacks on German industry reduced production to a mere 25 vehicles per month by the spring of 1945. By then, development of the Panther II was far advanced but the deteriorating war situation precluded commencement of production. Instead, German armaments firms included extra features of the Panther II, such as all-steel road wheels, into late-production Panther Model G vehicles.

Specialised Variants

The Germans produced small numbers of several specialised versions of the Panther tank. The standard Panther command

ABOVE *This view of a Panther Model D, which is painted in field grey, emphasises the size of the well-shaped hull frontal plate. Note also the tools, hawsers and tracking which are stowed on the upper hull side.*

tank (Sdkfz 167) possessed reduced ammunition stowage to make room for extra radio equipment, but unlike many earlier German command tanks, it retained its main armament and hence its full fighting capacity. The vehicle carried the standard Fu 5 radio mounted in the turret with a 2m (6 ft 7in) rod antenna, which produced an effective range of 8km (5 miles). In addition, the vehicle carried a hull-mounted long-distance Fu 8 radio supported by a 1.3m

(4ft 3in) star antenna mounted on the rear deck that was effective over distances of up to 65km (40 miles). German factories fitted out approximately one in ten Panthers as command tanks. Initially these modifications could only be completed on the production line, but from July 1944 all new production Panthers incorporated a bracket to allow the subsequent addition of extra radios and antennae, as well as a conversion kit to allow the transformation of standard tanks into command vehicles in the field. This modification greatly eased the problem of replacing lost command vehicles.

The Panther command tank (Sdkfz 168) was a more specialised vehicle, designed for use by Luftwaffe air-to-ground liaison officers. Externally similar to the standard Panther command tank, this vehicle carried a Fu 7 radio instead of the Fu 8. However, since Germany was on the defensive and the Luftwaffe was increasingly a broken arm, it is unclear whether the small number of Sdkfz 168 vehicles which were produced saw service in their intended role. Instead, it is more likely that they were used as conventional Panther command vehicles by armoured units. The Panther command tank was a success and their outward similarity to regular Panther tanks ensured that they were not easy to

pick out, the enemy having to look for the distinctive rear star aerial. The provision for field conversion after July 1944 also meant that there was normally sufficient command Panthers to meet tactical requirements.

Panther Armoured Observation Vehicle

The Germans also produced 41 Panzerbeobachtungspanthers, an armoured artillery observation variant of the Panther tank. The German Army allocated these vehicles to the single battalion within the armoured artillery regiment of each panzer division equipped with Wespe and Hummel self-propelled artillery vehicles. Hitherto, German artillery spotters had utilised half-tracks or a few specialised vehicles built on German or converted foreign tank chassis. These vehicles possessed a dummy gun instead of their main armament, together with a roof-mounted observation periscope and elongated radio antennae. The Panzerbeobachtungspanther, the prototype of which emerged in the summer of 1943, built

BELOW *A rear view of a Panther, vehicle 435, showing the sloped rear of the tank's hull. Note the two exhaust pipes in the centre with storage panniers on either side of them. (Panthers mounted two types of exhaust system and jack stowage.)*

on the chassis of a late Model D tank, had more sophisticated observation devices than earlier vehicles. First, the vehicle retained its main armament, an obvious advantage in combat. Second, the observation Panther mounted a stereoscopic range-finder inside its turret, and the vehicle commander possessed two periscopes, rather than one. These enhancements permitted more accurate artillery spotting, and despite its scarcity, this Panther variant was by far the most effective German wartime armoured observation vehicle.

Sparrowhawk Night-fighting Panther

The Germans also equipped a very small number of Panthers with special infra-red sights for night-time combat. The German Army had tinkered with infra-red night-sighting equipment early in the war, but it was only after the Allies had achieved aerial superiority by 1943 that the Germans returned to the project with vigour. That year, the Germans fitted small numbers of Panthers with a 300mm (11.8in) Uhu (Owl) infra-red searchlight and a Biwa image converter, which translated the infra-red image into perceptible light. During early trials at the Armoured School at Fallingboostel in Germany, Panther crews practised the intricacies of night-driving and targeting. The searchlight's effective range, however, was only about 600m (1968ft), which greatly limited the effectiveness of the Panther's superb gun.

ABOVE *Contrasting frontal and rear views of a pair of Panther tanks in a village square. The Death's Head symbol on the left hull front indicates that the vehicle belongs to the 3rd SS Panzer Division* Totenkopf. *The driver's sight flap is closed on the vehicle in the foreground.*

Therefore, in 1944, the Germans mounted larger 600mm (23.6in) infra-red searchlights on a half-track which was to be deployed alongside the Panther to provide greater illumination. Finally, alongside these two vehicles, the Germans planned to deploy a Falke (Falcon) half-track, carrying a panzergrenadier squad equipped with assault rifles that were intended to be fitted (though they never were) with Vampir (Vampire) night-sights. The German Army designated this combined three-vehicle tactical unit as the Sperber (Sparrowhawk) and the arrangement theoretically extended target range to 2500m (8202ft). During the summer of 1944, the Panthers of the 3rd Company, 24th Panzer Regiment, from the 116th Panzer Division, re-equipped with Owl devices at the Bergen training ground, where they also practised Sparrowhawk night-fighting techniques. Hitler intended to employ the company in the Ardennes counter-offensive and a few Sparrowhawk teams deployed to the Western Front, but they were never used in their designated role. One Sparrowhawk Panther team deployed to Stuhlwissenberg in Hungary early in 1945, with

ABOVE *A Panther Model A of the 5SS Panzer Division Wiking traverses its potent, long-barrelled 7.5cm gun to its right during defensive operations in the Soviet Union in May 1944. The Wiking Division was formed from 'Germanic' volunteers mainly from Scandinavia and Northwest Europe.*

the Sixth SS Panzer Army, for its counter-offensive intended to relieve beleaguered Budapest, but the rest of the company followed minus their infra-red devices.

During 1945, the Germans planned to equip a total of five Sparrowhawk companies, but this goal proved illusory. Two Sparrowhawk Panther teams, though, did join the *ad hoc* Panzer Division *Clausewitz*, which had been thrown together during the spring of 1945 on the Western Front. On 21 April these two Panther teams overran an American anti-tank hedgehog on the Weser-Elbe Canal, in the only documented combat employment of the Sparrowhawk night-fighting Panther. In March 1945 the Panzer Division *Muncheberg* also received a company of 10 Sparrowhawk Panther tanks and a half-track-mounted, mechanised infantry company equipped for night-fighting. The division fought in the final battle for Berlin where it was destroyed, but it is unclear whether the Sparrowhawks saw action in their designated role. The tank school at Fallingboostel also developed a more sophisticated employment of the Owl equipment, known as Solution B. The drawback of the Sparrowhawk system was that it provided night viewing capability only to the commander, who had to direct both the gunner and driver. Late in the war, Fallingboostel fitted a few old Panther Models D and A tanks with an extra

infra-red searchlight and an image converter for the driver, and converted one of the gunner's periscopes to night imaging, thus providing night viewing capability for three of the crew. During April 1945, several Solution B-equipped Panthers joined the Panzer Division *Clausewitz*. In mid-April, near Uelzen, in the only known employment of the Solution B-equipped Panther, these vehicles destroyed an entire platoon of the new British Comet tank. Work on a replacement for the Panther, designated the Panther II (or the Panther Model F) began during the spring of 1943, when the Army Weapons Department issued a design specification that the Panther's replacement should possess a maximum of interchangeable parts with the projected successor for the Tiger: the King Tiger. The most significant change intended for the Panther II was a completely redesigned small armoured turret which improved protection and which took significantly less time and resources to construct. This turret was designed to take both the standard 7.5cm KwK 42 L/70 gun of the Panther or the

8.8cm KwK 43 L/71 gun earmarked for the King Tiger. The deteriorating military situation, however, prevented the Panther II from entering production, and only a small number of prototype vehicles were built.

Bergepanther Recovery Vehicle

Both the weight and mechanical unreliability of early Panthers demonstrated the need for a heavy, fully tracked recovery vehicle, as it could take up to four 18-tonne (17.7-ton) artillery tractors to recover a disabled Panther tank. The Germans were unable to recover from the battlefield many of early Panthers disabled at Kursk; tank commanders often had to resort to using other Panther tanks to extricate disabled vehicles, but this placed such enormous additional strain on the towing Panther's already weak transmission that it frequently caused the breakdown of the towing Panther as well. Consequently, the German Army quickly forbade this practice and imposed heavy punishments on tank commanders caught misusing their Panthers in this fashion. Instead, tank units often impressed obsolete tanks as improvised recovery vehicles, with field workshops removing turrets and erecting winches and towing equipment.

Despite this, all of these expedient measures were imperfect and the obvious solution was a new purpose-built heavy recovery vehicle. The Panther chassis was the obvious candidate, although production demands of the Panther tank itself initially prevented design of a purpose-built Panther recovery vehicle. Despite this, in June 1943, MAN dispatched 12 standard Panthers direct from the factory, minus their turrets, to serve as towing vehicles with the two

Panther battalions earmarked for the Kursk offensive. Thereafter, Henschel designed and produced some 70 Bergepanther recovery tanks during July–August 1943. This vehicle utilised the basic Panther chassis minus turret which was replaced by a powerful, movable 40-tonne (39.4-ton) winch powered by the tank's electrical turret traverse system. An open wood and steel superstructure, together with a canvas roof cover, was all that protected the crew. A heavy earth spade was also hinged at the rear plate, for use as a counterbalance and lever. The winch worked well and its load capacity could be further increased by erecting a series of pulleys. The Germans planned to issue two Bergepanthers to every Panther battalion.

Overall, the vehicle proved a very successful recovery tank that was always in great demand, as it was powerful enough to recover not only the Panther, but even the heavier Tiger tank. Its armoured chassis was also popular with its crews, because it allowed recovery even under direct enemy fire, which became more common during 1944–45. In total, MAN and Henschel built some 350 Panther recovery vehicles.

Another use of the Panther was the integration of its turret directly into fortified defences. The turret was mounted on top of an underground pillbox and during the winter of 1944–45, the Germans raised special Pantherturm (Panther

BELOW *The Panther Model D sports brown-on-sand desert camouflage painted crudely over the original field-grey finish, patches of which are still showing. The vehicle's turret, in particular, illustrates well the rippled appearance of Zimmerit anti-magnetic mine paste.*

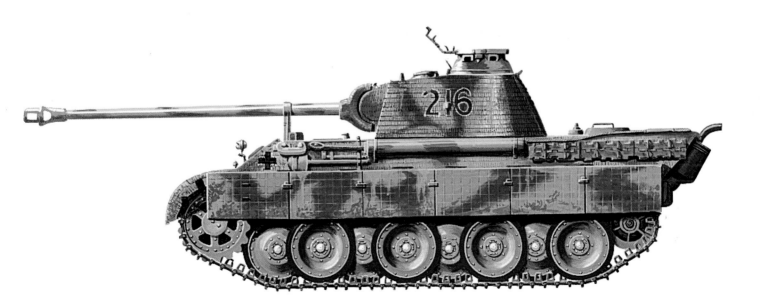

Manufacturer: MAN, Daimler-Benz, MNH, Henschel
Chassis Nos: 210001–210254, 211001–214000

850 produced from January to September 1943

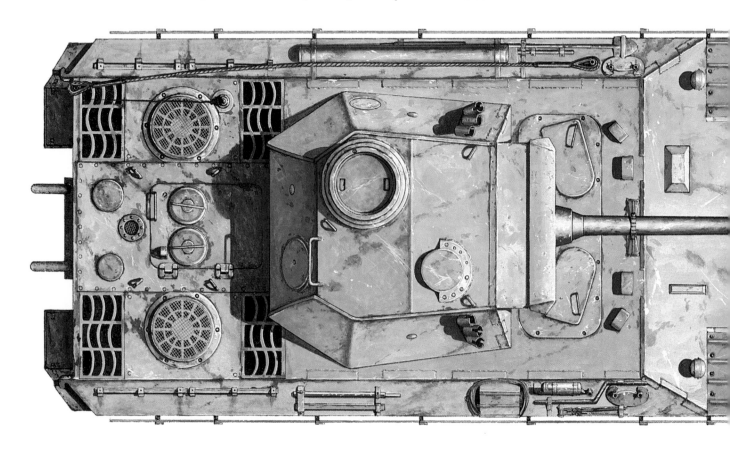

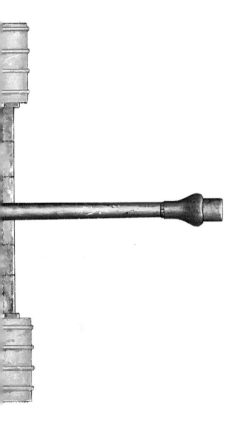

Combat service: **First saw action at Kursk, July 1943**
Issued to: **51st and 52nd PzAbt**
23rd and 26th Independent Panzer Regiments
1st and 2nd SS Panzer Divisions

SPECIFICATIONS: Panzer V Panther Model D (Sdkfz 171)

GENERAL
Vehicle Type: medium tank
Entered Service: spring 1943
Crew: five
Combat Weight: 43 tonnes (42.3 tons)

DIMENSIONS
Overall Length: 8.86m (29ft)
Hull Length: 6.88m (22ft 7in)
Width: 3.43m (11ft 3in)
Height: 2.95m (9ft 8in)

ARMAMENT
Main: 7.5cm (3in) KwK 42 L/70 gun
Secondary: 1 x 7.92mm (0.312in) MG
34; 1 roof-mounted

AMMUNITION STOWAGE
Main: 82 rounds
Secondary: 4200 rounds

ARMOUR
Hull Front (Nose): 80mm (3.2in)
(at 35 degrees)
Hull Front (Driver's Plate): 80mm
(3.2in) (at 35 degrees)

Hull Sides: 40mm (1.6in) (at 90 degrees)
Hull Rear: 50mm (1.6in) (at 60 degrees)
Turret Front: 100mm (4in)
(at 80 degrees)
Turret Sides: 45mm (1.8in)
(at 65 degrees)
Turret Rear: 45mm (1.8in)
(at 62 degrees)
Turret Roof: 15mm (0.6in)
(at 0–6 degrees)

MOTIVE POWER
Engine: Maybach HL 210 P30 V12-
cylinder petrol
Power: 650 bhp
Fuel Capacity: 730 litres (161 gallons)

PERFORMANCE
Maximum Road Speed: 46kph
(29mph)
Maximum Cross-Country Speed:
24kph (15mph)
Operational Range (Road): 177km
(110 miles)
Operational Range (Cross-Country):
89km (55 miles)

turret) fortress anti-tank companies and incorporated them into the Western Wall, as well as the Gothic Line defences in northern Italy. Another company, with 12 Panther turrets, also participated in the final defence of Berlin during April 1945. Damaged Panthers, or those immobilised for lack of fuel – an increasing reality in the last months of the war – were also dug in as static pillboxes. During the Ardennes counter-offensive, the Germans employed an unusual field improvisation of the Panther. A dozen Panthers were disguised, using thin metal sheets, to resemble the American M-10 tank destroyer and repainted in Allied camouflage patterns. These disguised Panthers joined small numbers of captured Allied vehicles in SS-Standartenführer (Colonel) Otto Skorzeny's 150th Panzer Brigade. Skorzeny's mission was to sow confusion and chaos in the American rear areas to facilitate the German advance beyond the Meuse River. The tactical advantage the Germans gained from this subterfuge was limited, however, and once the brigade lost the element of surprise, all its disguised Panthers were soon knocked out.

The Panther in Combat

In service, when properly maintained and handled, the Panther proved more than a match for the American Sherman, the British Churchill and Cromwell tanks, or the Soviet T34. It also retained a slight degree of superiority over the T34/85 – the up-gunned and up-armoured T34 tank that entered Red Army service in 1944. Although the Panther's substantial size and weight were limitations, its combination of a good road speed of 45kph (28mph), well-sloped armour, and a high-velocity gun made it a formidable opponent. The Panther was particularly effective in defence and during the quick, local counter-attacks at which the Germans excelled. In fact, the vehicle reflected a good compromise between a tank's competing needs for penetration, protection, speed, mobility, reliability and operational range.

The 7.5cm L/70 KwK 42 gun was an accurate high-performance gun with excellent penetration, capable of destroying any enemy tank in existence during 1943–44 at combat ranges of 2000m (6561ft). Firing armour-piercing rounds, the gun had a superb muzzle-velocity of 1120 metres per second (3675 feet per second) which allowed it to penetrate some 170mm (6.7in) of vertical armour at

BELOW *German troops wearing winter camouflage smocks crowd on top of a column of Panther Model D tanks advancing on a snow-covered road. Note the raised driver signal flaps on the left side of the tank's frontal hull plate.*

ABOVE *A snow-covered Panther Model D drives through the wrecked remains of a settlement, the tank commander standing up in his open turret cupola. Note the cover over the muzzle break fitted to the end of the long 7.5cm gun.*

1000m (3280ft), equal to that of the Tiger tank's larger 8.8cm gun. The high muzzle velocity of the Panther gun also gave it a very flat trajectory which made it highly accurate. Veteran Panther crews claimed a 90 percent hit rate at distances up to 1000m (3280ft). All in all, the KwK 42 L/70 was one of the most outstanding tank guns of World War II. At the same time, the Panther's armour was sufficient against Allied tanks and anti-tank guns at typical combat ranges. The vehicle's sloped 80mm- (3.2in-) thick frontal hull armour and 100mm- (3.9in-) thick turret front plates offered excellent protection; even the heavy American 9cm gun could rarely penetrate the Panther's frontal plate at distances above 1000m (3280ft). The Panther's weaker side and rear armour kept the vehicle's weight down, but left it vulnerable to flanking fire, which offered the best chance of destroying the vehicle. As the Panther entered widespread German service during 1944, it became a serious concern for Allied forces. While never gaining a reputation akin to the more formidable Tiger, the Panther saw far wider service than the Tiger and therefore constituted, in reality, a greater problem for the Allies.

Nonetheless, mechanical problems continued to plague the Panther throughout its service history. While the 650bhp (later 700bhp) Maybach petrol engine produced adequate power, it proved insufficiently rugged and rarely survived more than 1609km (1000 miles) before requiring rebuilding. The transmission also proved problematic and clutch failures were commonplace, especially early on. The petrol engine was also more combustible and consumed twice as much fuel as a diesel engine of similar size. However, the wide 660mm (26in) track effectively displaced the Panther's weight and ensured that it had lower ground pressure than the American Sherman tank. The Panther was consequently a relatively mobile tank for its size and weight.

The Panther battalion, progressively introduced into each panzer division during 1943–44, fielded 76 Panther tanks, divided into four companies of 17 vehicles, plus eight Panthers in the headquarters echelon. During 1943–44, German panzer divisions returned one of their tank battalions to the Reich where they re-equipped with the Panther and then underwent field trials before returning to their parent formation. The 1st Panzer Division was the first formation to be re-equipped, and by January 1944, some 15 panzer divisions fielded a Panther battalion. During the summer of 1944 Panther tanks also equipped 13 new single battalion-strong panzer brigades. By 1945, however, mounting losses and dislocated production had wrecked these organisational establishments, and the 1945 panzer division organisation authorised just a single mixed tank battalion of Panzer IVs and Panthers.

Panther Superiority

One of the better known Panther aces was SS NCO Ernst Barkmann, the commander of the 4th Company, 2nd SS Panzer Regiment, of the 2nd SS Panzer Division *Das Reich*. Barkmann had first commanded a Panther in 1943 on the Eastern Front where he became a veteran tanker. An exploration of his combat experiences in Normandy illustrates aptly the fighting qualities of the Panther. On 8 July 1944, Barkmann destroyed his first Sherman tank near St Lo and discovered his vehicle's superiority over the American tank. Four days later he destroyed two more Shermans and disabled a third. Later the same day, he knocked out a further three Shermans and an anti-tank gun before his Panther was damaged by an Allied anti-tank round. On 14 July, in a borrowed tank still stained with the blood of the previous commander, Barkmann notched up another three Shermans before an Allied artillery round blew off his track.

On 26 July, this time back in his own now-repaired Panther, Barkmann and the rest of the 2nd SS Panzer Regiment desperately resisted the breakout attempt made by the American Army during their Operation 'Cobra' offensive. His tank's carburettor broke down and the immobilised Panther was further damaged by American fighter-bombers. Frantic night-time repairs managed to get the vehicle running again by the next morning. Isolated from his company on 27 July, Barkmann tried to catch up but, south of Le Lorey, he unexpectedly encountered an American spearhead. Single-handedly Barkmann advanced to engage an enemy of unknown strength. Despite suffering repeated hits from enemy weapons that damaged the Panther's front drive sprocket, threw one track, put a hole in the hull, jammed a hatch and wounded the driver, his Panther remained in action. Barkmann's tank knocked out another nine Allied tanks in this engagement and was still able to limp away in reverse gear to fight another day. Incredibly, after improvised repairs had been made to his battered tank, Barkmann was back in action the next day where he added another six enemy tanks to his rapidly mounting tally. Wounded by shrapnel on 29 July, Barkmann's company were encircled by American forces at Gavray. His tank nevertheless managed to break through the American

cordon to reach new defensive positions – all while towing a disabled tank at the same time! Finally, on 1 August 1944. Barkmann's luck ran out when the ammunition in the disabled Panther he was towing blew up and set fire to his own vehicle, which had to be abandoned. On foot, his crew fought their way back through enemy lines to reach their parent division. For his exploits, both in and out of his Panther, the German High Command awarded Barkmann the coveted Knight's Cross.

From 1944, mounting Allied aerial mastery, especially in the Western theatre, increasingly threatened the Panther's battlefield superiority. Nonetheless, it remained the mainstay of the German panzer force until the end of the war. Consequently, the Panther was in the thick of the action in the final, desperate German efforts to prevent the fall of Berlin. During mid-April 1945, the Panther tank fought its last major engagement in any strength against Soviet armour that

had broken through the German defences, to advance across the Seelow Heights. Here, for the last time, a battalion of Panthers, supported by some Tigers, savaged massed Soviet armour. Fittingly enough, after Hitler had committed suicide, it was the last two remaining Panthers of the encircled Berlin garrison that spearheaded a final desperate breakout bid on 2 May 1945, to evade capture by the Soviets. Although both Panthers were lost, they helped to punch a tiny hole in the Soviet encircling ring that allowed small numbers of the garrison to fight their way west to surrender to American forces. Indeed, during 1944–45, the Soviets gained a very healthy respect for the Panther's combat power, and made great efforts to recover and repair disabled vehicles, so that the Red Army could deploy several Panther-equipped tank companies against the vehicle's inventors.

The Panther was thus a very good battle tank by the standards of World War II. It combined firepower, armour protection, and mobility into a first-rate fighting machine that remained generally superior to its opponents, until the 1945 appearance of the American M-26 Pershing and Soviet Josef Stalin heavy tanks. The planned Panther II would have further maintained its superiority. On the other hand the Panther had a number of serious shortcomings, most notably mechanical weakness and high fuel consumption, which reduced its strategic mobility. Developed in less than a year, the Panther was an impressive counter to the T34. It incorporated the best features of the Soviet vehicle, reflecting German willingness to replicate the technological achievements of its opponents.

CHAPTER 14

JAGDPANZER V JAGDPANTHER

The combination of lethal firepower, excellent well-sloped protection and good mobility made the Jagdpanther one of the most effective armoured fighting vehicles of World War II. But the vehicle was manufactured in too few numbers – only 392 were produced – to exert any significant impact on the battlefield.

I n mid-1943, the German Army Weapons Department ordered the development of a heavy tank destroyer, based on the chassis of the Panther tank, which was designated the Jagdpanzer V Jagdpanther (Hunting Panther). The High Command had selected this chassis as the only available, effective fully tracked platform for the powerful 8.8cm Pak 43/3 L/71. The hybrid Panzer III/IV chassis was insufficiently strong to bear the weight of a tank destroyer that mounted this gun, unless the superstructure armour was extremely light, and such a vehicle would not survive for long against the powerful Allied anti-tank guns in existence by 1943. The other potential chassis, that of the Tiger I, was too immobile to produce a good heavy tank

LEFT *This view of the Jagdpanther tank destroyer highlights both the steep reverse slope of the lower hull plate, and the large, smooth expanse of the vehicle's frontal plate. Note the vision slots for the driver which are situated on the right.*

destroyer, as the disappointing trials of the Panzerjäger Tiger (P) Elefant project had clearly demonstrated.

Development History

On 20 October 1943, the MIAG firm completed the first prototype Jagdpanther, designated the 8.8cm Anti-tank Gun 43/3 on Anti-tank Vehicle Panther. On 27 February 1944, as part of a simplification of armoured fighting vehicle designations, Hitler ordered that the vehicle be called simply the Jagdpanther. The general production vehicle comprised a standard Panther Model G tank chassis, fitted with a very well-sloped armoured superstructure. By 1944 standards, the vehicle possessed only modestly thick armour, which ranged from 80mm (3.2in) frontal protection, to 50mm (2in) and 40mm (1.6in) thick plate on the sides and rear, respectively. The Jagdpanther's well-sloped shape and low silhouette, however, provided the vehicle with excellent protection even though it possessed

BELOW *A column of Jagdpanthers advance across open terrain.*
The distinctive saukopf mantlet is clearly visible on the lead vehicle, as is
the well-sloped nature of the frontal plate. Note also the wide tracks for
good mobility and the uneven texture of the Zimmerit paste.

only moderately thick armour. Indeed, the steeply sloped superstructure and sleek, almost elegant, low profile made the Jagdpanzer V one of the most visually attractive armoured fighting vehicles of World War II.

Internal Workings

The inside of the tank was very popular with its five-man crew as well, despite its cramped interior (the huge breech mechanism of the Pak 43/3 and the ammunition racks taking up most of the space). Nevertheless, there was enough space to work in. Of the crew, the driver sat at the front left, while the wireless operator on the other side of the gun (he also operated the ball-mounted machine gun). Behind them sat the gunner and the loader, while to the rear of the compartment sat the commander. The main compartment hatch was in the rear wall of the

superstructure. Some of the crew could enter or leave by this hatch, but it also doubled as a loading hatch for long fixed-type ammunition. There was room inside the compartment for 600 rounds for the machine gun. Platoon commanders often had extra radio equipment installed and this addition was distinguished externally by two radio aerials to the rear of the superstructure.

An Effective Balance

The Jagdpanther weighed in at a substantial 45.5 tonnes (44.8 tons), but this did not significantly impede the vehicle's mobility, thanks to the powerful 700bhp Maybach HL 230 engine. With this power plant, the vehicle achieved an admirable 45kph (28mph) maximum road speed, and a top cross-country performance of 24kph (15mph) which compared favourably with other German tank destroyers of the period. This superb cross-country performance owed much to the vehicle's interleaved road wheel suspension and wide tracks. This combination produced a ground pressure figure lower than that of the StuG III assault gun – a vehicle that weighed half that of the Jagdpanther! Indeed, the excellent balance achieved in the Jagdpanzer V between lethal firepower, excellent protection and good mobility made the vehicle one of the most effective German armoured fighting vehicles of World War II.

The German MIAG factory alone manufactured Jagdpanthers between February and December 1944 until MNH joined the construction programme for a five-month period before all production ceased in April 1945. The Jagdpanther, however, remained a very rare tank destroyer since these firms delivered only 382 vehicles during this 15 month production-run, at an average of just 26 machines per month. That actual production never remotely approached

the planned completion target of 150 vehicles per month was due to the severe disruptions caused by repeated Allied bombing raids.

The Jagdpanther in Combat

During the 1944 Allied campaign in Normandy, the Jagdpanzer V remained an extremely rare vehicle with just 14 vehicles actually entering combat. The 654th Army Heavy Anti-tank Battalion was the only Jagdpanther-equipped German unit stationed in the West to engage the Allies during the summer of 1944. When the Allies landed in German-occupied France on D-Day, 6 June 1944, the 654th

SPECIFICATIONS: Jagdpanzer V Jagdpanther (Sdkfz 173)

GENERAL
Vehicle Type: heavy tank destroyer (heavy self-propelled anti-tank gun)
Entered Service: early 1944
Crew: five
Combat Weight: 45.5 tonnes (44.8 tons)
Chassis: Panzer V Panther

DIMENSIONS
Overall Length: 9.86m (32ft 4in)
Hull Length: 6.87m (22ft 6in)
Width: 3.28m (10ft 9in)
Height: 2.72m (8ft 11in)

ARMAMENT
Main: 8.8cm (3.5in) PaK 43/3 L/71 gun
Main Gun Traverse: 11 degrees left to 11 degrees right

Secondary: 1 x 7.92mm (0.312in) MG 34 in hull front

AMMUNITION STOWAGE
Main: 60 rounds
Secondary: 600 rounds

ARMOUR
Hull Front (Nose): 60mm (2.4in) (at 35 degrees)
Hull Front: (Driver's Plate) 80mm (3.2in) (at 35 degrees)
Hull Sides: 40mm (1.6in) (at 90 degrees)
Hull Rear: 40mm (1.6in) (at 60 degrees)
Superstructure Front: 80mm (3.2in) (at 35 degrees)
Superstructure Sides: 50mm (2in) (at 60 degrees)

Superstructure Rear: 40mm (1.6in) (at 60 degrees)
Superstructure Roof: 17mm (0.67in) (at 5 degrees)

MOTIVE POWER
Engine: Maybach HL 230 P30 V12-cylinder petrol
Power: 700 bhp
Fuel Capacity: 700 litres (154 gallons)

PERFORMANCE
Maximum Road Speed: 46kph (29mph)
Maximum Cross-Country Speed: 24kph (15mph)
Operational Range (Road): 210km (131 miles)
Operational Range (Cross-Country): 140km (87 miles)

Battalion was deployed at the Mailly-le-Camp training grounds near Paris. The unit had just received newly produced Jagdpanthers and its crews had begun familiarising themselves with these new vehicles. By 18 June, however, only two of the battalion's three companies had received its establishment of 14 Jagdpanthers. Furthermore, as the crews of one of these companies were insufficiently familiar with their new vehicles, just the 14 Jagdpanthers of the 2nd Company saw action in Normandy. Although this company only arrived late in the campaign, on 28 July 1944, the potent firepower possessed by its tank destroyers was to make an immediate impact on the battlefield. On 30 July, the 2nd Company played a crucial role in halting Operation 'Bluecoat', the attack launched by the British XXX Corps to widen the frontage of the breakthrough already achieved to their immediate right by the Americans at Avranches.

On 30 July 1944, just south of Caumont, the British 15th (Scottish) Division, supported by Churchill tanks of the 6th Guards Tank Brigade, burst through the weakened German line and advanced toward Hill 309. Suddenly two Jagdpanthers burst out of their cover in a small copse and, with covering fire provided by a third still-concealed vehicle, engaged the Churchill tanks. In an encounter lasting just two minutes, these tank destroyers knocked out 11 Churchill tanks before withdrawing in the face of superior Allied numbers. The company had to abandon two vehicles, however, after their tracks were damaged by Allied fire. Although these 14 Jagdpanthers had blunted this particular Allied advance, they could not prevent the imminent collapse of the entire German front in Normandy. In the maelstrom that engulfed the German Army in the West during August 1944, just two of the 2nd Company's Jagdpanthers managed to escape back across the River Seine.

The Jagdpanzer V would always remain a rare vehicle which was used by the Germans in penny-packets. The Ardennes counter-offensive was the only operation in which the German Army was to employ this tank in any strength. Some 51 Jagdpanthers were deployed in the Ardennes, no less than one-seventh of the total number ever produced. During this operation, Jagdpanthers typically equipped just one of the three companies found in each independent army heavy anti-tank battalion; the other two companies fielded assault guns or Jagdpanzer IV/70 tank destroyers. The Germans deployed six such battalions in combat in the Ardennes, all of which were well understrength and fielded less than their official complement of 14 Jagdpanthers. Chronic manpower and

equipment shortages like these dogged the entire German effort during their Ardennes counter-attack.

In such desperate circumstances, the German forces committed to the Ardennes relied heavily on the potent firepower of these 51 Jagdpanthers. On 20 December 1944, for example, the eight Jagdpanzer V and 25 Jagdpanzer IV/70(V) vehicles of the 560th Army Heavy Anti-tank Battalion provided intense fire support for the frenzied attacks made by the fanatical panzergrenadiers of the 12th SS Panzer Division *Hitlerjugend*. The High Command had allocated to this division the vital mission of smashing the Allied blocking positions at Dom Bütgenbach. Success here was urgently needed, so that the Germans could open up another axis of advance toward Malmédy and thus maintain the momentum of the offensive. Despite the tactical success achieved with the aid of these Jagdpanthers, the northern German thrust soon ground to a halt when Allied forces surrounded and destroyed the armour of the SS Battle Group Peiper.

Operation 'Northwind'
Not all of the 51 Jagdpanthers which had been deployed for the Battle of the Bulge actually took part in the offensive.

The High Command pulled the 654th Army Heavy Anti-tank Battalion out of reserve half-way through the attack and redeployed it to take part in Operation 'Northwind' (Nordwind) in Alsace-Lorraine on New Year's Eve 1944. This offensive involved a six-division thrust from the north that advanced southwards to Strasbourg in order to meet a southern German pincer movement which had been launched from the Colmar Pocket, the German-held salient jutting beyond the River Rhine onto French soil. The Germans hoped that their recapture of Strasbourg – a town which was imbued with great symbolic significance – would cause a rift between the French and the other Western Allies.

The eight operational Jagdpanthers of the 654th Battalion played a key role in the partly successful advance by the southern German pincer. However, despite the Jagdpanther's well-sloped armour and low profile, which provided excellent protection from Allied fire, the Germans still lost several of these tank destroyers during this operation. On 6 February 1945, for example, at Wolfgantzen near Colmar, one Jagdpanzer V had positioned itself in a small copse, ready to ambush a French armoured column.

ABOVE *This view of the Jadgpanther illustrates well both the vehicle's elegant, well-sloped profile, and the extent to which the long-barrelled 8.8cm gun overhung the front of the tank destroyer. Note also the missing section of the Schürzen side skirting, and the large interleaved roadwheels.*

However, the Jagdpanther was itself taken by surprise when Sherman tanks of the First French Army attacked it from both flanks simultaneously. The French Sherman tanks shot off both the Jagdpanther's tracks, thus disabling the vehicle. The crews of two other Jagdpanthers of the 654th Battalion also had to abandon their vehicles after engine failure and track damage, respectively. The Germans abandoned a fourth Jagdpanther after engine failure, although a recovery team, using a Bergepanther recovery vehicle managed successfully to tow the tank destroyer away for repair at a rear depot.

By the end of the ultimately unsuccessful Operation 'Northwind' counter-attack, the 654th Battalion fielded only four operational Jagdpanthers – just half of its original complement. By March 1945, this battalion had been wiped out in futile attempts to stem the inexorable Allied advance deep into the German Reich.

CHAPTER 15

PANZER VI TIGER I

Probably the best-known armoured fighting vehicle of World War II, the Tiger I tank was particularly feared by the Allies for its potent 8.8cm gun and heavy armour protection. Although the battlefield exploits of the Tiger were legendary, the tank itself was dogged by very poor mechanical reliability and possessed only limited mobility.

The German Panzer VI Tiger I heavy tank – probably the most famous tank of World War II – traces its immediate origins back to the German Army's reaction to its May 1940 combat experiences in the West. The damage inflicted by the few Allied heavy tanks that the Germans encountered, such as the British Matilda II at Arras and the French Char 1B at Flavion, prompted the Germans to step up their development of a heavy tank. Before this, the Germans had expended only modest developmental efforts during 1937–38 on a tank much heavier than the Panzer IV. By 1938, this effort had produced two prototype heavy tanks, the Breakthrough Tank 1 (DW1) and the VK3001. These programmes did not get far, however,

LEFT A Tiger I of the 101st SS Heavy Tank Battalion, attached to the 1st SS Panzer Division Leibstandarte SS Adolf Hitler, moves through a village on its way to the Normandy front in early June 1944. In the foreground is a Schwimmwagen amphibious jeep.

because the German Army was entirely satisfied with the capabilities and development potential of the Panzer IV.

Development History

During the spring of 1941, just before the German invasion of the Soviet Union, the Army Weapons Department stepped up existing development work on a heavy tank concept. During the summer of 1941, the German Army imbued these programmes with much greater impetus, after their initial experiences of combat against the Red Army's new T34 medium and KV heavy tanks. These modern Soviet tanks outperformed all existing German tanks, including the Panzer IV, and this prompted the Germans to develop a new medium tank (the Panzer V Panther) and a new heavy tank design that eventually became the Panzer VI Model E Tiger I.

During 1941, controversy dogged these reinvigorated German efforts to develop a new heavy tank. Hitler desired a future German heavy tank that mounted a modified

German 8.8cm anti-aircraft gun, whereas the Weapons Department favoured a tank that mounted a smaller 6cm or 7cm tapered-bore gun to keep down the vehicle's overall size and weight.

ABOVE A frontal view of a Tiger deployed in a wood. Note the extra sections of track carried on the hull nose and driver's plate. The poor slope of the Tiger's armour is evident on this vehicle, but it was enough to stop the majority of enemy anti-tank rounds.

Prototypes – Porsche and Henschel

This disagreement led to the commencement of work on two separate heavy tank prototypes. The Weapons Department contracted the first project, designated the VK3601, to the Henschel firm of Kassel. The contract specified that this vehicle should weigh 36–40 tonnes (35.4–39.4 tons) and mount a tapered-bore 6cm or 7cm gun. The Porsche firm received the second contract to produce a 45-tonne (44.3-ton) tank, designated the VK4501 that mounted an 8.8cm gun. The tapered-bore gun envisaged in the Henschel VK3601 project, however, required extensive use of tungsten steel, a commodity then in very short supply within the Nazi war economy. This scarcity forced the German Army to abandon the development of the tapered-bore gun and with it the entire

VK3601 project. Not wishing to waste the effort already put in by Henschel on the VK3601 project, the German Army awarded the company a new heavy tank development contract. Designated the VK4501 (H), this project utilised a modified version of the existing VK3601 chassis that mounted the same 8.8cm tank gun as the rival Porsche design. By autumn 1941, therefore, both Henschel and Porsche were competing directly on two parallel heavy tank prototypes that mounted a powerful 8.8cm gun.

By April 1942, Porsche and Henschel had completed their prototypes, now designated the VK4501 (P) and VK4501 (H), respectively. Hitler personally observed the trials of each prototype at Rastenburg in East Prussia on 20 April 1942, his 53rd birthday. The Henschel model both performed marginally better than the Porsche prototype and was considered by the Weapons Department to be better suited for mass production than its Porsche rival. Consequently, the Weapons Department issued several contracts to Henschel for the production of a total of 1500 vehicles. But even before the trials had taken place, Porsche had been given a contract to deliver 90 pre-production versions of their VK4501 (P) Tiger prototype. Subsequently, when the Weapons Department awarded the main contracts to Henschel, they also cancelled the 90-unit Porsche VK4501 (P) order. Again the Germans were loathe to waste these 90 partially completed Porsche Tiger chassis, and ordered the firm to complete them as platforms for the Elefant (Elephant) improvised heavy tank destroyer. The German Army designated the Henschel general production VK4501 (H) vehicle as the Panzer VI Model E Tiger I, although in February 1944 this was altered simply to the Panzer Tiger Model E.

Main Production Run

Production of the Tiger I tank commenced in August 1942 and, after a 23-month programme, deliveries ceased in June 1944. In total Henschel produced 1354 Tigers, of which the firm completed 100 during 1942, 780 in 1943 and 474 during the first half of 1944. The rate of production gradually increased from an average of 20 vehicles per month in the last five months of 1942, through 65 vehicles each month during 1943, to peak at 75 Tigers per month in the first half of 1944. Despite being in production for nearly two years, the total number of Tiger I tanks delivered was relatively small, and the tank remained a rare vehicle in German service. To a large extent, this rarity reflected the substantial time and resources required to produce a heavy tank that was as large and complex as the Tiger I.

Tiger I

The Tiger I was a squat, angular heavy tank which was not dissimilar in appearance to the smaller Panzer IV. The vehicle was operated by a five-man crew and weighed a massive 56 tonnes (55.1 tons). Early production Tiger Is were powered by the 642bhp Maybach HL 210 engine, although from vehicle 251 onwards this was replaced with the more powerful 700bhp Maybach HL 230 engine. The latter power plant enabled the Tiger I to achieve a reasonable maximum road speed of 38kph (23.5mph) and a more modest cross-country speed of 20kph (12.5mph). The tank mounted the

BELOW *A Tiger tank, pictured on the left, drives past the remains of Soviet equipment – including a burning Soviet T34 tank – in early July 1943, during the opening phases of the abortive German 'Citadel' Offensive at Kursk.*

powerful 8.8cm KwK 43 gun with a barrel length of 56 calibres, and was protected by 100mm (3.9in) frontal armour and 80mm (3.2in) side and rear armour.

Track System

The Tiger I was a huge tank, and in its operational mode was too wide to be carried on a standard German railway flat-car. To solve this problem, Henschel designed an ingenious two-track system for the Tiger. In combat the Tiger I utilised wide 725mm (28.5in) battle tracks, but when being transported by flat-car these were replaced with narrow 520mm (20.4in) transport tracks after the outer layer of road wheels had been removed. Similarly, since the Tiger was too heavy to cross many bridges, it was well-equipped with wading equipment, allowing the tank to move along the bed of a river submerged to a depth of 4.1m (13ft 6in). However, this expensive and little-used wading equipment was dropped after the first 495 vehicles as an economy measure. In early 1944, Henschel introduced major construction modifications to the Tiger I, as part of increasing efforts to standardise production with the Panther tank. These included the replacement of the rubber-tyred road wheels with resilient steel-tyred ones.

Specialised Variants

The Germans developed fewer specialised Tiger I variants than was typical with other tanks, mainly because the tank's chassis remained a relatively rare platform. Two of the specialised variants of the Tiger I were developed by Henschel's Kassel factory. One was a heavy self-propelled assault howitzer named the Sturmtiger, which mounted a short-barrelled 38cm (15in) mortar. From late 1943, 18 Tiger chassis were converted to carriers for 38cm assault mortars. The turrets were replaced with a built-up fixed superstructure. The main armament was adjustable manually, via a worm-and-wheel/rack and pinion drive, and was a radically different design from that of any similar projector seen before. The 38cm (15in) mortar fired 376kg (761lb) HE projectiles out to a range of 6000m (19,685ft). As the projectiles were so heavy a small demountable crane was used to lift them. Fully loaded the Sturmtiger carried 13 rounds, but the fire rate was quite low because the mortar tube could only be loaded at zero elevation. In fact, the whole operation of loading required four men, including the gunner, while the entire crew consisted of five. The Sturmtiger saw only limited action – indeed it is said that the only useful employment the Sturmtiger ever found was

in the destruction of the Warsaw ghetto, though seven were present during Operation 'Wacht am Rhein'.

Another specialised variant was the Bergepanzer recovery tank. Because a full complement of tractors was not always available to a battalion, initially the only recourse was to employ operational Tigers to tow away disabled tanks. This was not

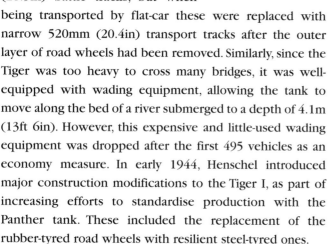

necessarily a last resort as it made sense to use tanks rather than unarmoured tractors in the field of fire. However, the practice led to the loss of dozens – perhaps even hundreds – of Tigers.

Wherever possible, any captured enemy tanks were used as recovery vehicles. A very few Tiger tanks were thus also modified as Bergepanzer Tiger recovery vehicles.

The Germans also constructed in small numbers two similar Tiger command vehicles, both of which were practically identical to the standard production Tiger tank, except for the addition of a powerful and advanced transmission system – the tank's air-cooled petrol engine driving a generator to drive the tracks by means of two independent electric motors – and longitudinal torsion bar suspension.

Performance

In terms of overall performance, the Tiger I was a formidable tank protected by heavy armour and mounting a powerful gun. This excellent combination of firepower and protection, however, was only achieved at the expense of a very limited mobility. The underpowered and mechanically unreliable Tiger I performed badly over rough terrain, consumed fuel at alarming rates and suffered from very slow turret traverse. To be fully effective the Tiger needed a well-trained crew and extensive expert maintenance.

Although the Tiger often performed superbly on the battlefield, at other times the vehicle failed to achieve its

SPECIFICATIONS: Panzer VI Model E Tiger I (Sdkfz 181)

GENERAL
Vehicle Type: heavy tank
Entered Service: late 1942
Crew: five
Combat Weight: 56 tonnes (55.1 tons)

DIMENSIONS
Overall Length: 8.24m (27ft)
Hull Length: 6.20m (20ft 4in)
Width (Operational): 3.73m (12ft 3in)
Width: (Transport): 3.15m (10ft 4in)
Height: 2.86m (9ft 5in)

ARMAMENT
Main: 8.8cm (3.5in) KwK 36 L/56 gun
Secondary: 2 x 7.92mm (0.312in) MG 34;
1 coaxial in turret; 1 hull front. 6 x smoke
dischargers.

AMMUNITION STOWAGE
Main: 92 rounds
Secondary: 3920 rounds

ARMOUR
Hull Front (Nose): 100mm (3.9in)
(at 66 degrees)
Hull Front (Driver's Plate): 100mm
(3.9in) (at 80 degrees)
Hull Sides: 60–80mm (2.4–3.2in)
(at 90 degrees)
Hull Rear: 82mm (3.2in) (at 82 degrees)
Turret Front: 100–110mm (3.9–4.3in)
(at 80 degrees)
Turret Sides: 80mm (3.2in)
(at 90 degrees)
Turret Rear: 80mm (3.2in)
(at 90 degrees)

Turret Roof: 26mm (1in)
(at 0–9 degrees)

MOTIVE POWER
Engine: Maybach HL 230 P45 V12-cylinder
petrol
Power: 700 bhp
Fuel Capacity: 534 litres (118 gallons)

PERFORMANCE
Maximum Road Speed:
38kph (24mph)
Maximum Cross-Country Speed:
20kph (12.5mph)
Operational Range (Road):
100km (62 miles)
Operational Range (Cross-Country):
60km (37 miles)

ABOVE *A Tiger tank painted with whitewash winter camouflage designed for combat in the arctic-like conditions of the Soviet winter. The vehicle's multi-layered, interleaved roadwheels and extra-wide tracks helped prevent this heavy tank's ground weight ratio from being too excessive.*

true tactical potential, thanks to the steady decline in crew standards and workshop facilities during the last year of the war. But by this time, however, the Tiger I was also being eclipsed by the more lethal firepower, better sloped protection, and superior mobility displayed by a new generation of formidable heavy tanks such as the German King Tiger, the American M-26 Pershing and the Soviet Josef Stalin vehicles.

The Tiger in Combat

The Tiger I tank first entered operational service in August 1942. Hitler's tank experts wished to conduct extensive trials in Germany on the first production vehicles, to test their reliability, and also to build up a considerable reserve of Tigers for use as a devastating surprise weapon in the forthcoming German offensive on the Eastern Front the following summer. But Hitler cast aside this sound advice.

In August 1942, Hitler ordered the first unit that had been equipped with the Tiger – the 1st Company, 502nd Heavy Tank Battalion – to be rushed immediately to the Eastern Front. On the 29th of that month, at Mga near Leningrad, the Tigers of this unit made their operational debut. The company's one 7.5cm-gunned Panzer III Model N and four Tiger I tanks had only just left the trains that had

carried them from the Reich, when German field commanders – following Hitler's orders – rushed them into action.

Hitler had committed the Tigers to operations in terrain which was totally unsuited to the use of heavy tanks, and all were disabled. The veteran Soviet units facing them maintained their resolve, even though their guns could not penetrate the thick frontal armour of these new German tanks; instead, the Soviets aimed their anti-tank guns at the Tigers' tracks and disabled them in this manner. Thus, Hitler's impatience threw away the element of surprise and the psychological impact that would have been achieved by deploying in mass such a formidable new weapon as the Tiger tank.

In December 1942, the Germans rushed the 503rd Heavy Tank Battalion to the southern section of the Eastern Front, in response to the successful Soviet counter-offensive that had surrounded General Paulus' Sixth Army at Stalingrad. Hitler was again so desperate to send this unit into action, that it was dispatched when only at half-strength. Yet even just a few Tigers could still exert a powerful influence on the battlefield, with five Tigers of the 502nd Battalion knocking out 12 Soviet T34 medium and T60 light tanks near Leningrad on 29 December 1944.

The Tiger in North Africa

The Western Allies encountered their first Tiger I tanks in Tunisia in December 1942. On 1 February 1943, during the German thrust along the Robaa-Pont du Fahs road, the

British captured their first intact Tiger tank which presented them with valuable intelligence on the vehicle's tactical capabilities. On that day, a mixed German battle group of motorised infantry supported by 18 tanks – mostly Panzer III and IV vehicles but led by two Tigers – ran into prepared British defences. British six-pounder guns of the 72nd Anti-tank Regiment, RA, engaged the Tigers at ranges as close as 375m (1230ft). The Tiger I captured by the Allies was knocked out after receiving 10 six-pounder hits, two of which achieved major penetrations of the 80mm- (3.2in-) thick side armour. Subsequent scientific tests showed that the Tiger's frontal armour was invulnerable to British six-pounder fire except at point-blank range, although the recently developed British 17-pounder gun had a better chance of penetrating the tank's armour at normal combat ranges. These tests also suggested that if its armour was penetrated, the Tiger I, like many other German tanks, was prone to burn fiercely due to ignition of its fuel and ammunition.

It was a standard German tactic in North Africa, unlike the action at Robaa, to deploy Tigers to the centre-rear of armoured wedges to give fire support to the lighter Panzer III and IV tanks, while other vehicles secured the flanks against Allied anti-tank guns. German combat experience with Tigers in the desert showed that their great weight made necessary extensive reconnaissance of the terrain over which they were to operate. In particular, bridges in Germans hands often had to be reinforced to permit their use by Tigers. Together with the vehicle's immense fuel consumption, these factors restricted the tactical flexibility with which German units employed the Tiger.

The Tiger in Italy

One engagement, during the 1944 Allied campaign in Italy, highlights the difficulties the Germans faced thanks to the poor cross-country performance, mechanical unreliability and the sheer physical bulk of the Tiger I tank. Between 23 and 25 May 1944, the 16 Tigers of the 3rd Company, 506th Heavy Tank Battalion fought a costly engagement around Cori. On 23 May, the company advanced across a railway embankment and engaged Allied armour, but during the crossing three Tigers were disabled, two with track problems and one with gearbox failure. The Tiger's 2.02m (6ft 8in) barrel-overhang also proved a problem, as two other Tiger tanks accidentally jammed their guns into the soil as they came down the steep-sided embankment and had to be towed clear. Eventually 13 Tigers continued the advance during which they knocked out six Sherman tanks. During this attack, however, Allied artillery damaged another Tiger which withdrew back to a German workshop. The next day Allied anti-tank fire disabled another Tiger which was blown up by its crew.

The company was then ordered to withdraw. While five Tigers held back an Allied attack, the remaining six tanks tried

BELOW *This Tiger tank, vehicle 142, has been painted with a desert camouflage scheme. The gun, rather unusually, has been draped with netting and further netting is stowed along the hull side. Note the smoke dischargers towards the top front of the turret side.*

to tow away the three disabled Tigers by the embankment. However, the strain caused four of the six towing Tigers to break down. The Germans then had to destroy the three disabled tanks by the embankment and use the remaining two Tigers to tow back the four that had broken down. By the time the company had withdrawn to Cori, two of its five rearguard tanks had been disabled (one by Allied fire and the other because of a gearbox fault) while one of the two towing tanks had also broken down. Hence, while the three operational rearguard Tigers continued to block the Allied advance, back at Cori the company commander could deploy just one working Tiger and six disabled ones. With the

rearguard now unable to stop the Allied advance into Cori, and with recovery vehicles unable to reach the company in time, the commander ordered the destruction of the six disabled Tigers to prevent them falling into Allied hands, while his remaining four tanks withdrew north. The company had lost 12 Tigers, but only three had been disabled by Allied fire. Clearly, the Tiger's mechanical unreliability was more of a threat than Allied fire.

The Tiger in Normandy
The Allied experience of engaging the Tiger I tank during the Normandy campaign confirmed their fears that this

similar silhouettes of the Tiger and the smaller Panzer IV when viewed from long range.

The Tiger I, in fact, saw service with just four German units during the entire battle for Normandy. The 316th Heavy Tank Company of the Panzer *Lehr* (Demonstration) Division deployed just two Tigers, while the 101st SS, 102nd SS and the German Army 503rd Heavy Tank Battalions each deployed a maximum of 45 Tiger tanks. In a vain attempt to halt the spread of 'Tiger-phobia' in the ranks, General Montgomery banned all combat reports that recounted the tank's prowess as prejudicial to British morale. This phobia was observed by one brigadier, who noted that on 12 June 1944 a solitary German Tiger tank fired for a whole hour and was then able to drive off unmolested, as not one British tank was prepared to engage it. The British soon developed the dictum that not only would five Shermans be needed to knock out a Tiger, but also that four of them would be destroyed in the process. However, that the Allies were justified in their awe of the Tiger was demonstrated by several encounters during the Normandy campaign, most notably by the actions of panzer ace Michael Wittman at Villers Bocage.

Wittman Destroys a Brigade

Perhaps the most famous wartime exploit of the Tiger I was the bloody defeat Wittman's Tigers inflicted on the British 7th Armoured Division – the famous Desert Rats – at Villers Bocage. This engagement, which has been recounted in many differing versions, has passed into somewhat exaggerated legend as the tale of how Wittman's single Tiger destroyed an entire brigade! The Tiger tanks involved belonged to the 2nd Company, 101st SS Heavy Tank Battalion, commanded by SS Lieutenant (Obersturmführer) Michael Wittman, one of the German Army's leading tank aces. By Wittman's death in Normandy on 8 August 1944, the Germans had credited him with 119 'kills' on the Eastern Front, plus another 20 in Normandy. The High Command rewarded Wittman for these achievements with the coveted Knight's Cross with Swords and Oak Leaves.

On 13 June 1944, Wittman was carrying out a reconnaissance in his own command Tiger, when he spotted the British 22nd Armoured Brigade of the Desert Rats Division advancing south to outflank the neighbouring German formation, the Panzer *Lehr* Division. Wittman,

vehicle was a formidable weapon in a more static defensive role, where its mechanical unreliability was less significant. With its thick armour and powerful gun, the Tiger I soon became the scourge of Allied forces in Normandy. The tank became so feared by British troops (who faced nearly all the Tigers the Germans deployed) that senior commanders became acutely concerned at the extent of 'Tiger-phobia'. One manifestation of this fear was that Allied troops reported sightings of Tigers all over the front: yet in reality, no more than 90 Tiger I tanks were present in the theatre at any given moment, and then only in selected sectors of the front. These exaggerated sightings of Tigers reflected the

ABOVE *Tigers of the 101st SS Heavy Tank Battalion, part of the I SS Panzer Corps, drive along a French road. Note crossed-key insignia on the right of the hull front. This column is advancing towards the Normandy front-line in early June 1944.*

hidden in a wood, was astonished at the complacency with which the British advanced on that hazy day before they stopped for a tea-break. Wittman's gun-layer, SS-Oberscharführer (Sergeant) Woll growled that their enemy was acting as if they had won the war already! But what could Wittman's solitary tank, plus the other four operational Tigers of his company deployed nearby, do to stop this dangerous British advance?

Without hesitation, Wittman sprang into action. His tank, together with the four other Tigers, cut behind the British brigade's 'A' Squadron and advanced westward down the hill

to enter the town of Villers Bocage. Here Wittman knocked out three Churchills of the 22nd Brigade's HQ Squadron, although a fourth managed to escape, only to be knocked out a few minutes later as Wittman headed east back up the hill to deal with 'A' Squadron. After approaching 'A' Squadron from the rear, Wittman's tank burst out of a wood and advanced firing along the British column. Within two minutes his tank had destroyed 12 British vehicles. Soon Wittman's other four Tigers had joined this battle, with a further eight Tigers from the 1st Company, 101st SS Battalion, giving support from a distance. At the end of this engagement 28 vehicles belonging to 'A' Squadron of the County of London Yeomanry, part of 22nd Armoured Brigade, were left burning, and the squadron itself had been virtually destroyed.

Wittman's tank, two other Tigers and a newly arrived Panzer IV then turned west to return to the centre of Villers

Bocage. Here, a Sherman Firefly tank mounting the powerful 17-pounder gun, three Churchill tanks and a six-pounder anti-tank gun had positioned themselves in side streets in order to ambush the Tigers at close range. The anti-tank gun engaged Wittman's Tiger from a side alley and immobilised it, before the third Tiger rammed the corner building, collapsing the masonry on top of the British gun. The Firefly then knocked out the second Tiger tank and the Panzer IV. Wittman and his crew were forced to fight their way out of the battle on foot; only the lack of Allied supporting infantry allowed them to avoid capture. In total, four Tiger tanks were knocked out by the furious resistance put up by the Desert Rats. But despite these losses, the German riposte at Villers Bocage was one of the finest feats of combat of the Normandy campaign. Just 13 Tigers flung back and severely mauled an entire British Brigade, destroying 48 vehicles and inflicting 255 casualties.

A Tiger Tossed into the Air

In Normandy, however, not everything went as well for the Tiger I as it had at Villers Bocage, and even these heavy tanks proved vulnerable to the massive firepower which the Allies could deploy. On 18 July 1944, Montgomery commenced Operation 'Goodwood', his great armoured assault to outflank Caen from the east. In preparation for the offensive, 2000 Allied bombers obliterated the German defences, in conjunction with an artillery bombardment fired by 700 guns. This combined bombardment was so powerful that it even catapulted into the air one of the

56-tonne (55.1-ton) Tigers belonging to Lieutenant Baron von Rosen's platoon of the 503rd Heavy Tank Battalion. The vehicle landed turret-down on the ground and it took von Rosen's men three hours to get the turret hatch open to rescue the three surviving members of the five-man crew. The effects of this massive Allied bombardment were equally devastating for the rest of von Rosen's crews: one of his men was driven insane, while another committed suicide rather than continue to endure the Allied bombardment. Despite this terrible introduction to the realities of fighting the Allies in Normandy, the Tigers of the 503rd subsequently still managed to knock out 30 Sherman tanks, and they played a key role in halting the British armoured onslaught in 'Goodwood'.

Last Successes in Normandy

By 8 August 1944, the German front in Normandy was creeping closer to collapse as the Allied forces wore down the German defence. But even as the Allies closed in on the town of Vire that day, the Tigers of the 1st Company, 102nd SS Heavy Tank Battalion were able to score one last tactical success.

The Tiger I tank of SS-Unterscharführer (Corporal) Willi Fey smashed a British tank column, destroying 14 out of its

BELOW *A Tiger sporting desert brown-on-sand camouflage in North Africa. Note that on this vehicle the spare track sections are stowed on the side of the turret – a practice less common on this tank type than on the King Tiger.*

ABOVE *A column of Tigers advances through the extremely muddy terrain which was created by the autumn rain on the Eastern Front. In the foreground a Tiger tank commander is standing in the vehicle's turret with the cupola hatch open.*

15 Shermans. Later that day, Fey's Tiger knocked out a fifteenth Sherman with his last two rounds, although his tank was then immobilised by an Allied anti-tank round and had to be towed back to a rear depot by two other Tigers.

That same day other Tigers of the 1st Company knocked out a further nine Allied tanks, to produce a total of 24 Allied tanks destroyed by a single Tiger company in a single day! Temporary German tactical successes such as these, however, could not avert the catastrophe engulfing the Germans in Normandy, as the Allies successfully encircled them at Falaise. Very few of the 102nd SS Battalion's Tigers escaped the devastation inflicted on the German Army at Falaise, while none managed to get back across the River Seine during the frantic German retreat of late August 1944. Despite losing all its Tigers, the 102nd SS claimed to have destroyed no less than 227 Allied tanks in just six weeks of combat in Normandy!

The Eastern Front

During 1943–44, the Tiger I also built up a formidable record on the Eastern Front, where it was regularly called upon by the German Army to stem the advance of massed Soviet armour. By mid-1944, however, the Tiger was becoming outclassed by the new Soviet heavy tanks of the Josef Stalin (JS) series. When Tiger I tanks engaged Soviet JS-II tanks for the first time at Targul Frumos, Romania, in May 1944, the Germans discovered to their horror that their 8.8cm guns could only penetrate the armour of the JS-II at ranges under 1800m (5905ft), at which distance the Tiger was vulnerable to the Soviet tank's powerful 12.2cm gun. Similarly, by early 1945 the Germans had recognised that the Tiger's gun could only penetrate the frontal armour of the new JS-III tank at ranges below 500m (1640ft), whereas the JS-III could penetrate the Tiger's armour at a range of 2000m (6561ft). Moreover, by the last 18 months of World War II, the degree of protection offered by the poorly sloped armour of the Tiger I was being reduced by the increasingly effective Allied anti-tank and heavy tank guns then entering service.

Tiger Losses

Given that Tiger I production ceased in June 1944 after completion of just 1350 vehicles, and that casualty rates rose steadily during the following six months, the Tiger I already

BELOW *A view of the rare Bergetiger recovery vehicle. As existing towing vehicles struggled to recover disabled Tigers from the battlefield, the Germans converted a few Tiger tanks into dedicated recovery vehicles by replacing the main armament with a powerful winch.*

RIGHT *Rear view of a column of Tiger tanks carrying paratroopers during German defensive operations against the Soviet summer offensive in Lithuania on 20 August 1944. Note the helmets hung on the extra tracking stowed on the left side of the turret.*

had become a very rare vehicle by the end of 1944. The number of Tiger I tanks the Germans fielded during the war peaked at 631 in June 1944, but this had dwindled to only 243 by the end of that year. For during the summer of 1944, the German Army lost nearly all of the 130 Tigers deployed in the West, and by the Ardennes counter-offensive, the army deployed just 23 Tiger I tanks along the entire Western Front. Hence, during the Battle of the Bulge, the Germans employed 52 of the new Panzer VI Model B King Tiger tanks, but just a single Tiger I, which was lost during the offensive.

Combat losses had reduced the 480 Tiger I tanks fielded both in the East and in Italy, in June 1944, to a mere 210 vehicles by December 1944. Overall, Tiger I strengths further plummeted to only 185 vehicles by February 1945. During March, the German Army suffered such enormous tank losses as the Allies overwhelmed its forces that by 1 April 1945 a combined total of just 70 Tiger I and King Tiger tanks remained operational.

The Swan Song of the Tiger

By March 1945, as the Allies advanced deep into the Reich, the Germans in desperation threw into the fray their very last resources. By closing and mobilising their training schools, the Germans flung instructors, raw recruits and any training vehicles available into the fighting in a last gasp effort to avoid defeat.

In the West, the 500th Heavy Tank Training Battalion was mobilised from the Paderborn armoured school, with seven old Tiger I and 10 King Tiger tanks that had been used for instruction. The battalion was flung in to stop two massive Allied pincers meeting and surrounding the vital Ruhr industrial zone, but could do little to stem the Allied onslaught and was destroyed in the attempt. Meanwhile, in the East, the Panzer Division *Muncheberg* – at brigade strength at best – was raised from various training school staffs and deployed a few Tiger I tanks which had been used for research purposes. This formation fought desperately near Berlin to halt the rapidly advancing Soviet tank armies, until it too was destroyed. It is clear that the very few Tiger I tanks that remained operational in the last two weeks of the war went down fighting along with the rest of the German Army.

CHAPTER 16

PANZER VI B KING TIGER

The extremely potent main armament of the King Tiger, as well as its heavy, well-sloped armour, made it the most feared German tank in the minds of the Allies. But the vehicle entered German service too late in the war and in too few numbers to prevent ultimate Allied victory in May 1945. It was, nevertheless, a formidable fighting machine.

The last major tank that the German Army developed and used operationally during World War II was the Panzer VI Model B Tiger II, usually referred to as the King Tiger (Königstiger) or Royal Tiger. This heavy tank was a logical development of the Panzer VI Tiger I that incorporated many of the excellent design features of the Panzer V Panther medium tank, including well-sloped armour. In appearance, the King Tiger's angled armour gave it more than a passing resemblance to the smaller Panther tank. Though a formidable weapon, the King Tiger remained a very rare vehicle as only 489 saw service with the German Army during the last 14 months of World War II. But thanks to the combination of the King Tiger's lethal firepower, its

LEFT This frontal view of a King Tiger illustrates well both the great length of the vehicle's overhanging 8.8cm gun and its well-sloped hull armour. The crew have rather half-heartedly camouflaged the tank with foliage.

virtual invulnerability to Allied fire and its sleek angular shape, this tank made a greater impression on Allied minds than the actual number of vehicles in service really warranted. Indeed, if anything, Allied fear of the King Tiger exceeded even that of the Tiger I.

Development History

The direct origins of the King Tiger can be traced back to the outcome of the Führer conference of 26 May 1941, just before the German invasion of the Soviet Union. The conference decided that the German Army Weapons Department should speed up existing research and development programmes on heavy tanks in the 35–45 tonne- (34.4–44.3 ton-) class being carried out by the firms of Henschel and Porsche. At this time, the Weapons Department also instructed Krupp to produce an improved tank gun version of the famous 8.8cm FlaK 41 anti-aircraft weapon. In the summer of 1941, these development projects

ABOVE *The uneven, cement-like finish of Zimmerit anti-magnetic mine paste is particularly evident on this King Tiger, as is the width of the vehicle's operational tracks. On the turret sides are brackets for extra track sections to be stored.*

were given further impetus by the shock of the first German combat encounters with the formidable new Soviet T34 medium and KV heavy tanks. From this period on, the goal of German heavy tank projects was to produce a vehicle that would possess greater firepower and better protection (in the form of well-sloped armour) than any Soviet tank then in existence – and any vehicle that the Soviets might develop in the immediate future. Consequently, in August 1942, the Weapons Department issued formal contracts for Porsche and Henschel to produce designs for a heavy tank that met these requirements.

By late 1942, Porsche had begun work on three prototype vehicles, designated the Panzer Tiger P2, which included a Krupp-produced turret mounting the 8.8cm KwK 43 L/56 gun used in the Tiger I. Porsche never completed these vehicles, however, partly because the firm fell into disfavour with the Nazi hierarchy, but also because the transmission of the Tiger P2 required large amounts of copper, a resource in short supply by late 1942.

Work by Henschel on prototype vehicles, termed the Tiger H3, was delayed by frequently changing design

specifications. In January 1943, Hitler personally intervened to insist that the protection on these King Tiger prototypes be upgraded to 185mm- (7.3in-) thick armour on the front, as well as 80mm (3.2in) on the sides. Other design modifications were also made in order to standardise parts with the Panther II tank development project, as the Germans belatedly recognised the benefits of increased standardisation of production.

In October 1942, the Weapons Department contracted Henschel to produce 176 King Tigers that mounted a new longer-barrelled 8.8cm gun, designated the Pak 43/3 L/71. After the orders for the rival Porsche Tiger P2 were cancelled in November 1942, Henschel was contracted to build a total of 526 tanks. By the end of the war, the Weapons Department had placed orders with Henschel's Kassel factory to construct 1500 King Tiger tanks. The first 50 production vehicles featured the turret already produced by Porsche for its now cancelled Tiger P2 programme. The Porsche turret, with its obvious rounded front and commander's cupola offset to the left, was instantly distinguishable from the solid, bluntly sloping form of the general-production Henschel turret. Once the Kassel factory had installed the 50 Porsche turrets already in existence, the turret was discontinued because trials suggested that the curved front might deflect enemy rounds down into the vulnerable junction where the turret and the hull top met.

After the completion of three pre-production vehicles in December 1943, Henschel delivered the first three production models in January 1944. During the next month eight King Tigers rolled off the Kassel production line, alongside 95 Tiger I tanks. Gradually, through 1944, Henschel switched its production efforts from the Tiger I to the King Tiger, until construction of the older tank design ended in June 1944.

By March 1945, when King Tiger manufacture ceased after a 15-month run, Henschel had delivered 489 King Tigers, including 20 command tanks. Construction targets rose steadily from under 45 vehicles per month in the first half of 1944, up to a peak of 120 tanks during October 1944. In reality, however, actual production fell far short of scheduled targets. Actual monthly construction peaked in August 1944 at only 94 tanks, while cumulative production totals fell well behind the schedule of 659 vehicles to be delivered by March 1945. These delays were caused by the five bombing raids the Allies launched against the Kassel factory between 22 September and 7 November 1944; by the fifth attack, the factory was virtually a ruin. These attacks wrecked King Tiger production – in comparison with the 94 tanks manufactured in August 1944, Henschel only completed 26 out of a scheduled 120 vehicles during October 1944.

The King Tiger was a heavy tank that weighed a massive 69.4 tonnes (68.3 tons). Its main armament comprised the magnificent long-barrelled 8.8cm KwK 43/3 L/71, whose barrel length was no less than 5.8m (19ft) – longer than a Panzer III tank! The vehicle carried 84 rounds for this gun, including 22 rounds housed in the turret rear and another 48 rounds stored in internal horizontal panniers along the hull side. Close-range defence was provided by two MG 34 machine guns, one mounted coaxially in the turret and the second in a ball mounting in the hull-front glacis plate. Furthermore, the commander's cupola had a fitting so that an extra external anti-aircraft machine gun could be added.

A Well-earned Reputation

The King Tiger enjoyed an excellent standard of frontal protection thanks to its 185mm (7.3in) turret face armour and its well-sloped 150mm- (5.9in-) thick hull glacis armour set at 40 degrees. The tank's sides and rear were also more than adequately protected by 80mm- (3.2in-) thick armour set at angles of between 60 and 80 degrees. The King Tiger's

BELOW *This King Tiger, vehicle 104, looks a little worse for wear after recent combat service. The tank has lost its Schürzen side skirts, patches of Zimmerit have come off, and parts of its towing hawser are dangling from the rear of the vehicle's right hull side.*

ABOVE *The frontal view of a King Tiger sporting a two-tone pattern field camouflage illustrates well the square, blunt face of the Henschel production turret. One section of spare tracking has been stored on the brackets fixed to the turret sides.*

massive bulk was powered by the formidable 700bhp Maybach HL 230 P V12-cylinder petrol engine. This power plant permitted the tank to reach a reasonable top road speed of 38kph (24mph), although the vehicle's maximum cross-country performance was a less impressive 17kph (10.5mph). Given its massive fuel consumption, the King Tiger had to carry large quantities of fuel – some 860 litres (189 gallons) – just to obtain a modest operational range of 110km (68 miles) by road and a mere 85km (53 miles) cross-country.

The King Tiger enjoyed a well-earned reputation for invulnerability among the Allied armies of World War II. The tank's 150–185mm (5.9–7.3in) frontal armour was virtually impregnable to any Allied tank or anti-tank gun – there is no surviving evidence to confirm that any Allied round penetrated the vehicle's frontal armour. The King Tiger's 80mm (3.2in) side and rear armour, however, could be penetrated at typical combat ranges by several Allied rounds, including the British 17-pounder tank and anti-tank gun. The Soviet T34/85 medium tank could penetrate the King Tiger's side armour at ranges under 1500m (4921ft)

and so could the JS heavy tanks at even greater ranges. Of course, King Tigers could also be immobilised by damage to their tracks caused by Allied fighter-bombers, artillery or infantry anti-tank weapons. Many King Tigers were lost during German retreats either due to mechanical failure or lack of fuel.

The King Tiger enjoyed an even greater reputation for lethal killing power than the Tiger I. The King Tiger's longer 8.8cm gun could penetrate the Allied Sherman and Cromwell tanks from any angle at over 3200m (10,498ft). However, the massive weight and heavy fuel consumption made the King Tiger a relatively slow and immobile vehicle, particularly as virtually no bridge could support it. The King Tiger was also dogged with early teething troubles, especially an overstretched drive system, so that mechanical reliability was initially poor. Indeed, the first five production vehicles, delivered to the Panzer *Lehr* (Demonstration) Division, had to be destroyed without ever entering combat in Normandy because of chronic mechanical unreliability. Consequently, the King Tiger – like the Tiger I – came into its own tactically as a static fire support asset in fixed defensive actions.

Command Vehicle

As part of the main King Tiger production run, Henschel produced 20 command vehicle variants of the tank. This command tank carried fewer main armament rounds – a total of 63 instead of 84 - in order to make space for the extensive radio equipment that was carried. The King Tiger command variant existed in two forms; the first was equipped with a 30 Watt Fu 8 transmitter in the turret in addition to the usual 10 Watt radio, while the second carried a 20 Watt Fu 7 radio transmitter instead of the Fu 8.

The King Tiger in Combat

The King Tiger was issued to just a select few army and Waffen-SS independent heavy tank battalions. These units were typically held in reserve at corps level and allotted to support subordinate divisions as necessary. The German Army dispatched 468 King Tiger tanks to combat units and utilised another 21 for training and development purposes. The total number of King Tigers in service with the German Army gradually rose from five in March 1944, up to 175 in September 1944. High casualty rates and disrupted production reduced this figure to 145 by November 1944, although recovering production increased King Tiger numbers to a peak of 219 vehicles in February 1945.

Only 13 German combat units were allocated King Tigers: a company of the Panzer *Lehr* Division; nine independent German Army heavy tank battalions - the 500th Training, 501st, 503rd, 505th-507th, and 509th-511th; and all three SS independent heavy tank battalions,

originally numbered 101st-103rd. In March 1944, the 319th Heavy Tank Company of the Panzer *Lehr* Division received the first five general-production King Tigers completed, the Panzer *Lehr* being the only German division to receive these tanks as part of its official War Establishment. The Company was equipped with remote control tankettes fitted with demolition charges, and it was with these tankettes that the company's five King Tiger and two Tiger I tanks were designed to operate. The next unit that the German Army equipped with King Tigers was the 503rd Heavy Tank Battalion. In June 1944, this unit was refitting in Germany after losing most of its Tiger Is, when it received its first batch of 12 King Tigers. The Germans deployed the unit to France in late June 1944, after it had received another 12 newly produced King Tiger tanks. Practically all these vehicles were lost in the cataclysm that engulfed the German Army in the West during August–September 1944.

The next unit to receive King Tigers was the 1st Company, 101st SS Heavy Tank Battalion. The German Army allocated 14 vehicles to this unit in late July and early August

BELOW *This disabled Henschel-turreted King Tiger has been abandoned at the side of the road by its crew after losing its right track. The King Tiger was a formidable fighting machine, but many never reached the front due to mechanical problems.*

1944, as replacements for Tiger I tanks lost in the Normandy battles. All these King Tigers were lost in the frantic German retreat across France during the late summer of 1944. The German High Command withdrew the 506th Heavy Tank Battalion from the Eastern Front to re-equip it in the Reich with a full complement of 45 King Tigers, thus making it the German Army's most potent armoured battalion. The German Army deployed the 506th to Holland in September 1944, where the unit's massive tanks helped to smash the heroic resistance of the 1st British Airborne Division at Arnhem bridge during the Allied 'Market-Garden' offensive. Subsequently, the 506th fought continuously on the Western Front until the German surrender on 8 May 1945. This battalion was unusual in that it was one of very few units equipped with King Tigers to receive regular replacement vehicles, being issued 25 new vehicles in three batches. Normally, as King Tigers rolled off the production lines, they went straight to re-equipping units stationed in

ABOVE *This famous photograph encapsulates the role of King Tigers in the Ardennes counter-attack. Tank 222 of the 501st SS Heavy Tank Battalion, attached to the Kampfgruppe Peiper, is at the Kaiserbarracke crossroads, just south of Peiper's axis of advance.*

Germany, rather than as replacements to heavy tank battalions already at the front.

In September 1944, the German High Command withdrew to Germany the remnants of the 101st SS Heavy Tank Battalion (now redesignated the 501st SS – resulting in confusion with the army heavy tank battalion of the same number) to outfit it entirely with newly produced King Tigers. By early December 1944, the German Army had earmarked the 501st SS for its Ardennes counter-offensive (the Battle of the Bulge), but due to sluggish production, caused by Allied bombing, the battalion had by then only received 28 King Tigers – 17 short of its full complement. The German High Command realised that Henschel would not complete more vehicles in the next two weeks, and so were forced to recall the 11 King Tigers already dispatched to the 509th Heavy Tank Battalion for re-allocation to the 501st SS – the Germans were robbing Peter to pay Paul! Yet even after receiving these additional tanks, the 501st SS still commenced the Ardennes counter-offensive with just 30 King Tigers, after nine of its tanks suffered mechanical failure during the unit's redeployment to the front. During this futile German attempt to throw the Western Allies back and recapture Antwerp, the battalion lost 13 of its 30 King Tigers.

The Battle of the Bulge

The Battle of the Bulge is the one battle of World War II most closely linked in popular perception with the King Tiger tank. In reality, the vehicle's actual role in this offensive was more modest than is commonly believed. Three independent heavy tank units fielded King Tigers for the German Ardennes counter-offensive: the German Army's 506th Battalion and 306th Company, together with the 501st SS Battalion. Together, these units deployed 52 King

Tigers, nearly one-third of the total number then in German service. The 501st SS deployed 30 King Tigers plus a solitary Tiger I, while the other two units each fielded 11 vehicles.

The best known German unit involved in the Battle of the Bulge was the SS Battle Group Peiper, the spearhead force of the 1st SS Panzer Division *Leibstandarte Adolf Hitler*. The King Tigers of the 501st SS had been attached to the *Leibstandarte* and were included in Peiper's Battle Group. The mission of SS Obersturmbannführer (Lieutenant-Colonel) Joachim Peiper's battle group was to exploit any success as rapidly as possible in order to develop the offensive towards Antwerp before the Allies could react. The terrain over which Peiper's forces would fight was very poor, consisting of just a few narrow, winding roads in the hilly and heavily wooded terrain of the Ardennes. The massive bulk and ponderous mobility of the King Tiger was

BELOW *British POWs bring up supplies to the crews of the 1st Company, 503rd Heavy Tank Battalion. The unit, fielding tanks with Porsche turrets, is deployed in a wood in Normandy during July 1944 to seek safety from the devastating power of Allied fighter-bombers.*

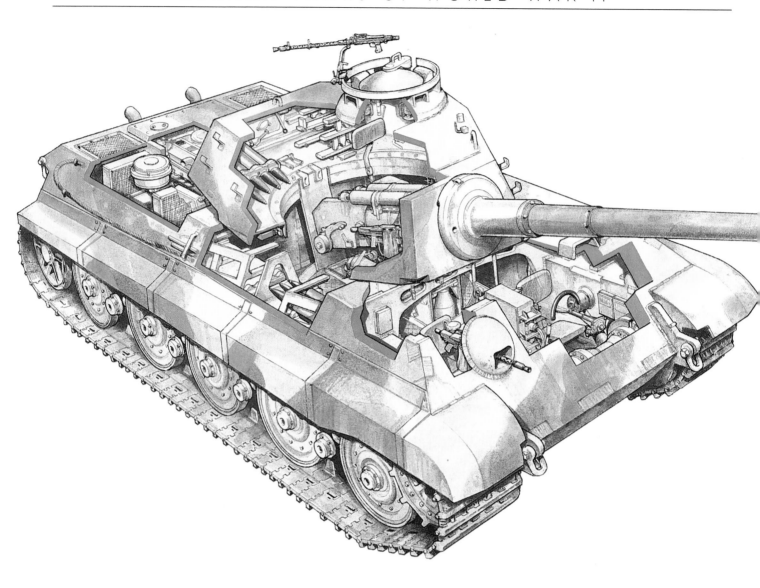

SPECIFICATIONS: Panzer VI Model B King Tiger (Sdkfz 182)

GENERAL
Vehicle Type: heavy tank
Entered Service: early 1944
Crew: five
Combat Weight: 69.4 tonnes (68.3 tons)
[first 50 Porsche turret vehicles
69.7 tonnes (68.6 tons)]

DIMENSIONS
Overall Length: 10.26m (33ft 8in)
Hull Length: 7.26m (23ft 10in)
Width (Operational): 3.75m (12ft 4in)
Width (Transport): 3.27m (10ft 9in)
Height: 3.09m (10ft 2in)

ARMAMENT
Main: 8.8cm (3.5in) KwK 43/3 L/71 gun
Secondary: 2 x 7.92mm (0.312in) MG 34;
1 coaxial in turret; 1 hull front. Fitting for

anti-aircraft 7.92mm MG 42 on turret roof;
smoke dischargers

AMMUNITION STOWAGE
Main: 84 rounds
Secondary: 5850 rounds

ARMOUR
Hull Front (Nose): 100mm (3.9in)
(at 40 degrees)
Hull Front (Driver's Plate): 150mm
(5.9in) (at 40 degrees)
Hull Sides: 80mm (3.2in)
(at 65–90 degrees)
Hull Rear: 80mm (3.2in) (at 60 degrees)
Turret Front: 185mm (7.3in)
(at 80 degrees)
Turret Sides: 80mm (3.2in)
(at 69 degrees)

Turret Rear: 80mm (3.2in)
(at 70 degrees)
Turret Roof: 44mm (1.7in)
(at 0–10 degrees)

MOTIVE POWER
Engine: Maybach HL 230 P30 V12-cylinder
petrol
Power: 700 bhp
Fuel Capacity: 860 litres (189 gallons)

PERFORMANCE
Maximum Road Speed: 38kph (24mph)
Maximum Cross-Country Speed:
17kph (10.5mph)
Operational Range (Road): 110km
(68 miles)
Operational Range (Cross-Country):
85km (53 miles)

particularly unsuited to such a mission in this terrain. Consequently, Peiper sensibly led his battle group with a mixed battalion of the more mobile Panzer IV and V tanks, placing the King Tigers at the very rear of his armoured column with instructions for them to keep up with the spearhead tanks as best they could. Not surprisingly, Peiper's King Tigers soon got left behind.

Six King Tigers of the 501st SS advanced somewhat further to the south to avoid traffic congestion in the rear of Peiper's forces. With them they each carried up to 20 German paratroopers of the 3rd Parachute Division into the battle. It is these few King Tigers that are depicted in the captured German ciné film which encapsulates the popular image of the King Tiger's role in the offensive. These few vehicles soon became involved in the bitter – and ultimately futile – German attempts to capture the bridge at Stavelot and open up another route of advance.

Back on Peiper's main axis of advance, however, it was only when the progress of his battle group faltered beyond Stoumont, on 20 December 1944, that 10 King Tiger tanks caught up with his Panzer IV and V spearheads. By the next day, Peiper had been surrounded at La Gleize by Allied counter-blows and was cut off from further logistic resupply. By the night of 23–24 December, Battle Group Peiper had ran out of fuel and ammunition and was forced to fight its way out on foot. The force abandoned 35 tanks – including six King Tigers – and deliberately disabled them to avoid their falling intact into Allied hands. Battle Group Peiper had been virtually destroyed. On Boxing Day 1944, the unit was dissolved, the remnants being reabsorbed into their parent formation, the *Leibstandarte*, which was pulled out for reorganisation and rest.

The 501st SS Heavy Tank Battalion lost 13 King Tigers during the frantic engagements fought by Battle Group Peiper, the desperate nature of the fighting being demonstrated by the massacre of 77 Allied prisoners by Peiper's men near Malmédy. At the time, Allied propaganda made much of the awesome power of their aircraft in knocking out 13 of these mighty tanks, but in reality most had already been abandoned by the Germans after engine failure, traffic accidents, track damage, or lack of fuel, before Allied aircraft attacked and destroyed them.

The collapse of Peiper's northern thrust, however, did not spell the end of the efforts demanded of the *Leibstandarte* by the German High Command. As the Allies began to recover, the Germans sought to maintain the initiative by switching their point of main effort further south to the area

around Bastogne. The town had been surrounded earlier in the offensive, but the Germans could not destroy this pocket due to determined Allied resistance, epitomised by the blunt reply – "Nuts!" – made by the American commander when invited by the Germans to surrender. By Boxing Day 1944, the Allies had managed to link up with the Bastogne garrison. The German Army now redeployed the *Leibstandarte*, with its remaining 17 King Tigers and solitary Tiger I, to Bastogne to help German efforts to encircle the town.

In the battles around Bastogne, the 501st SS lost its solitary Tiger I plus another three King Tigers, two of which were destroyed by Allied fire. Several other King Tigers were lost by the 506th Heavy Tank Battalion and 306th Tiger Company in the fighting in the southern half of the Ardennes offensive. One King Tiger of the 506th was knocked out by tanks of the American 6th Armoured Division, after being hit by eight armour-piercing rounds. In total the Germans lost 20 King Tigers in the Battle of Bulge – 40 per cent of the original force committed. Of these losses, however, only five tanks were lost directly to Allied fire, with most of the others being abandoned for a variety of other reasons.

With the defeat of the Ardennes counter-offensive, the last great King Tiger action in the West had been fought. Yet, occasionally, King Tigers still made significant contributions to the desperate defence the Germans conducted in the West during the last weeks of the war. The last 13 tanks ever produced at Henschel's Kassel factory, for example, were collected literally at the factory gates in late March 1945 by two recently raised units, the 510th and 511th Heavy Tank Battalions. These units used these newly produced vehicles to augment the four King Tigers previously used for development purposes which they had already acquired. Fielding just 17 heavy tanks between them, these two understrength units were flung desperately into the frontline to stem the Allied tide sweeping over central Germany in the last month of the war.

The King Tiger on the Eastern Front

The King Tiger was just as prominent in the savage fighting on the Eastern Front during 1944–45 as it was in the West. The first unit to employ King Tigers on the Eastern Front was the German Army's 501st Heavy Tank Battalion. The unit had originally been equipped with Tiger Is but had been decimated during heavy fighting in 1944, and was outfitted in Germany in August with a full establishment of 45 King Tigers. After being heavily engaged on the Eastern Front, the unit was all but destroyed in the Soviet offensive of January 1945.

During August 1944, the German High Command also re-equipped the 505th Heavy Tank Battalion with a full complement of King Tigers, and then dispatched the unit back to the Eastern Front. Next, the German Army's 503rd Battalion (later renamed *Feldherrnhalle*) followed to Germany for refitting, before being rushed off to Hungary in mid-October 1944. By January 1945, the 509th Heavy Tank Battalion had received its full establishment of 45 King Tiger tanks, after losing its original 11 vehicles when the High Command re-allocated them to the 501st SS Battalion before the Battle of the Bulge. The German Army then rushed the 509th by train to Hungary to take part in Operation 'Awakening of Spring'. This German offensive sought both to rescue the encircled German forces in Budapest and to drive the Soviets away from last oil fields still in Axis hands. The 509th was accompanied to Hungary on 12 January 1945 by the battle-weary 501st SS Battalion, exhausted by its exertions in the Ardennes.

Rather unusually, the German Army held the 503rd SS Heavy Tank Battalion at training grounds in Germany for over a year, awaiting new production King Tigers. By January 1945, it had been issued with 39 heavy tanks and was then rushed to central Poland to help shore up the German front that was disintegrating in the face of the Soviet Vistula-Oder offensive. Desperate defensive fighting on the borders of the German Reich itself reduced this unit to just two operational tanks by 20 March 1945. The last King Tiger unit that the High Command dispatched to the Eastern Front was the 502nd SS Battalion, which received 31 King Tigers between 14 February and 22 March 1945. The unit was then rushed off to Bohemia to help Army Group Centre stave off the final Soviet onslaught on the Reich. The ferocity of the battles into which these King Tiger units were hurled is attested to by the fact that, in the four months between October 1944 and January 1945, some 57 King Tigers (one-ninth of the total produced) were lost in the East.

Special Operations

In addition to the King Tiger's fine frontline combat record, the vehicle's impressive bulk also proved useful in special military operations of a more political nature. On 20 September 1944, for example, Adolf Hitler tasked his special operations expert, SS Standartenführer (Colonel) Otto Skorzeny, with keeping Hungary – Germany's Axis ally – in

the war against the Soviets. On 15 October 1944, the Hungarian regent, Admiral Miklos Horthy, ordered his troops in Budapest, the Hungarian capital, to man their defences and announced an imminent armistice with the Soviets. In Operation 'Panzerfaust', Skorzeny's SS forces undertook a stunning coup to seize Budapest to prevent Horthy's regime surrendering or defecting to the Soviets. The backbone of Skorzeny's forces comprised the SS Raiding Unit Centre plus

RIGHT *The tanks of the 503rd Heavy Tank Battalion, newly equipped with 43 King Tigers at the Sennelager training grounds in Germany, line up for inspection. Vehicle 300 belongs to the commander of the 3rd Company.*

the elite commando-parachutists of the 600th SS Paratroop Battalion. Supporting this force were 35 King Tiger tanks belonging to the German Army's 503rd Heavy Tank Battalion, recently re-equipped with these vehicles at the Sennelager training grounds in Germany. Skorzeny's commandos, supported by these tanks, daringly stormed the Burgberg fortress, the seat of the Hungarian government, in a stunning coup-de-main that lasted just 30 minutes. With the seat of government in their control, the Germans were able to impose a new Hungarian Fascist regime loyal to Hitler, under the leadership of Ference Szalasi. Unfortunately, this audacious operation could not stabilise the deteriorating German strategic situation on the Eastern Front. Although Szalasi's pro-Nazi regime survived until May 1945, by late December 1944 the Red Army had surrounded Budapest and the Hungarian Army was deserting en masse to the Soviets.

JAGDPANZER VI JAGDTIGER

The massive Jagdtiger – the heaviest armoured fighting vehicle to enter operational service during World War II – possessed a lethal 12.8cm gun and was almost invulnerable to Allied fire. However, the Germans completed only a few Jagdtigers and this, together with the vehicle's lack of mobility, ensured that this tank destroyer made little tactical impact on the battlefield.

It was the normal policy of the German Army, in the latter half of World War II, to produce from its combat tanks a tank destroyer variant that mounted a larger main armament in a limited-traverse superstructure. Such a policy was aimed at maximising the number of armoured fighting vehicles that the Germans could deploy on the battlefield, as turretless armoured fighting vehicles were both quicker and cheaper to produce than tanks. The King Tiger tank was no exception to this practice, and a heavy tank destroyer vehicle was duly produced on its chassis. This vehicle, which was designated the Jagdpanzer VI Jagdtiger (Hunting Tiger), was truly a giant armoured fighting vehicle. It had the distinction of being the heaviest German tank

LEFT This top view of a Jagdtiger shows the box-like superstructure fitted onto a modified King Tiger chassis. The vehicle's four turret top periscopes are clearly visible, as are the hull gunner's and driver's periscopes on the hull front.

destroyer of World War II and that it carried the largest gun to be mounted in any operational, German, fully tracked armoured vehicle.

Development History

A full-scale mock up of the Jagdpanzer VI Jagdtiger appeared in October 1943, just six months after its tank forebear – the King Tiger – had entered full-scale production. Subsequently a prototype vehicle emerged and, after successful field trials, the Weapons Department placed a contract for 150 vehicles with the Austrian armaments firm of Steyr-Daimler-Puch at St Valentin in Austria, which became the sole producer of the Jagdtiger.

The chassis of the Jagdtiger was in effect simply a slightly extended version of the standard King Tiger platform. Steyr-Daimler-Puch vertically extended the hull sides of this tank chassis to form the superstructure fighting compartment, or barbette, within which the main armament was housed.

In appearance, the Jagdtiger was squarer and taller than the Jagdpanther, and the former bore an obvious resemblance to the King Tiger tank on which design it was based, although it lacked the latter's graceful curves. However, the Jagdtiger's high profile – the vehicle measured 2.82m (9ft 3in) in height –unfortunately presented a large target to the enemy.

The Jagdtiger carried the massive 12.8cm Pak 44 L/55, the largest gun mounted in any operational German wartime tank or tank destroyer. This gun had superb performance and produced a muzzle velocity of 920 metres per second (3016 feet per second) with both high-explosive and armour-piercing rounds. Indeed, the Jagdtiger fired high-explosive rounds with a greater muzzle velocity than the

SPECIFICATIONS: Jagdpanzer Jagdtiger (Sdkfz 186) (Henschel vehicle)

GENERAL
Vehicle Type: heavy tank destroyer
Entered Service: late 1944
Crew: six
Combat Weight: 71.7 tonnes (70.6 tons);
Porsche Vehicle: 69.9 tonnes (68.8 tons)
Chassis: Panzer VI Model B King Tiger

DIMENSIONS
Overall Length: 10.66m (34ft 8in);
Porsche Vehicle = 10.37m (34ft)
Hull Length: 7.80m (25ft 7in)
Height: 2.82m (9ft 3in);
Porsche Vehicle = 2.92m (9ft 7in)
Width: 3.63m (11ft 11in);
Porsche Vehicle = 3.59m (11ft 9in)

ARMAMENT
Main: 12.8cm (5in) PaK 44 L/44 gun.
(Some vehicles 8.8cm (3.5in) PaK 43/3 L/71.)

Main Gun Traverse: 10 degrees left to 10 degrees right
Secondary: 1 x 7.92mm (0.312in) MG 34 in hull front

AMMUNITION
Main: 38 rounds
Secondary: 2925 rounds

ARMOUR
Hull Front (Nose): 100mm (3.9in) (at 40 degrees)
Hull Front: (Driver's Plate): 150mm (5.9in) (at 40 degrees)
Hull Sides: 80mm (3.2in) (at 90 degrees)
Hull Rear: 80mm (3.2in) (at 60 degrees)
Superstructure Front: 250mm (9.8in) (at 75 degrees)
Superstructure Sides: 80mm (3.2in) (at 65 degrees)

Superstructure Rear: 80mm (3.2in) (at 80 degrees)
Superstructure Roof: 30mm (1.2in) (at 0 degrees)

MOTIVE POWER
Engine: Maybach HL 230 P30 V12-cylinder petrol
Power: 700 bhp
Fuel Capacity: 865 litres (190 gallons)

PERFORMANCE
Maximum Road Speed: 38kph (24mph)
Maximum Cross-Country Speed: 17kph (10.5mph)
Operational Range (Road): 170km (106 miles)
Operational Range (Cross-Country): 121km (75 miles)

ABOVE *Side view of the late-production Jagdtiger, distinguishable from the Henschel version by the fact that its suspension was based on eight sets of roadwheels instead of nine. The Porsche suspension was lighter than the Henschel's, a useful economy in a tank that was already too heavy.*

famous German 8.8cm Pak 43 anti-tank gun, while possessing only a slightly inferior armour-piercing performance. Moreover, the Jagdtiger's gun had a maximum range of 22,410m (73,523ft) which was substantially greater than that of the Pak 43. Firing armour-piercing rounds, the Jagdtiger could penetrate an astounding 230mm (9.1in) of armour at 1000m (3028ft). Even at long range – 3000m (9842ft) – the Jagdtiger's main armament could still penetrate an incredible 173mm (6.8in) of armour. Put simply, no Allied armoured fighting vehicle was safe from the Jagdtiger's extremely powerful gun!

Armament Capacity

Originally, the Germans had developed the 12.8cm Pak 44 as a super-powerful anti-tank gun to augment the Pak 43. Production of a suitable platform for the Pak 44 gun, however, was seriously delayed during 1944, and it appeared as if the gun would not enter active service in its original role for many months. Consequently, the Armaments Ministry diverted the first six months' production of the gun to the Jagdtiger programme. If the Pak 44 had been used in its intended role, this superb anti-tank gun soon would have earned a reputation as a tank killer which would have surpassed that of the famed 8.8cm anti-tank gun.

The great punch of the Jagdtiger was undermined, however, by its limited ammunition capacity, which at just

38 rounds for the main armament was one of the poorest loads of any German wartime armoured fighting vehicle. This poor armament stowage capacity resulted from the great weight of the 12.8cm rounds which were so heavy that they had to be split into two easily assembled sections; a necessary measure that nonetheless unavoidably slowed the Jagdtiger's rate of fire.

Not every Jagdtiger, however, enjoyed the luxury of mounting this formidable weapon. By the start of 1945, the 12.8cm gun was in such short supply that Steyr-Daimler-Puch was forced to mount the 8.8cm L/71 KwK 43 gun, normally carried in the King Tiger tank, in the last 26 of the 77 Jagdtigers completed. The Jagdtiger's 12.8cm main armament possessed the usual degree of traverse seen in most German tank destroyers of this period: a vertical elevation of between +15 and -7.5 degrees and a horizontal traverse of 10 degrees left and right. Just as with all turretless armoured fighting vehicles, to engage targets beyond this field of fire the entire vehicle had to be slewed around. This drawback was the inevitable tactical consequence of the German imperative to boost overall production rates, by concentrating on cheaper turretless armoured fighting vehicles, rather than tanks. In addition to the main armament, the Jagdtiger carried a standard ball-mounted 7.92mm MG 34 in the hull for close defence purposes. The tank destroyer also possessed a fitting for an external 7.92mm anti-aircraft MG 42 to be mounted on the engine compartment roof. This provision reflected the increasing danger that Allied air power presented to German armour in the last 18 months of the war.

Armour

The Jagdtiger's armour protection was as massive as its main armament. The vehicle sported no less than 250mm-(9.8in-) thick armour set at 75 degrees on the superstructure front, that rendered the Jagdtiger invulnerable to frontal attack by any Allied tank or anti-tank gun. The superstructure sides and rear were more modestly armoured with 80mm- (3.2in-) thick steel, while the bolt-on superstructure roof had only 30mm (1.2in) armour. Consequently the Jagdtiger could still be knocked out by enemy hits on the sides or rear, and of course the vehicle remained vulnerable to disablement by Allied artillery or aerial attack. If this armour was not enough, following the practice used on the King Tiger, crews fitted spare track sections on to the turret-side for added protection. It was principally this heavy armour that raised the weight of the Jagdtiger to a colossal 71.7 tonnes (70.6 tons), making it the heaviest armoured fighting vehicle to see operational service in World War II.

A crew of six manned this beast of a tank destroyer – the largest crew of any wartime German armoured fighting vehicle that entered service. The Jagdtiger was powered by the same 700bhp Maybach HL 230 TR V12-cylinder engine utilised in the Tiger I, King Tiger and Jagdpanther. But even this impressive power plant could not adequately power such a bulky vehicle and as a result the vehicle had only limited mobility. Though capable of a reasonable top road speed of 38kph (24mph) it could only manage a maximum speed of 17kph (11mph) cross-country. An enormous rate of fuel consumption, even when travelling by road – of 5 litres per kilometre (1.8 gallons per mile) – further limited the Jagdtiger's mobility, making the vehicle one of the most fuel-hungry German vehicles of the war.

The first production Jagdtigers possessed the standard Henschel-designed King Tiger suspension based on transverse torsion bars and nine axles with interleaved road wheels. Subsequent vehicles had a simpler Porsche longitudinal torsion bar suspension, based on eight axles with smaller overlapping road wheels grouped in pairs. The simpler Porsche suspension reduced production time in a German armaments industry increasingly desperate to maximise production. The Porsche suspension also had the advantage of being lighter, usefully reducing the weight of this overloaded armoured fighting vehicle by 1.8 tonnes (1.77 tons). A further limit to the Jagdtiger's combat value was the reality that virtually no bridge in Germany could bear the vehicle's immense load.

A Rare Vehicle

Despite the substantial interest that the Jagdtiger generated with the Allies at the time and with the public ever since, the vehicle remained one of the rarest armoured fighting vehicles of World War II. In reality, Steyr-Daimler-Puch completed just 77 Jagdtigers, only half of the original order. This was largely due to the disruption of production occasioned by repeated Allied bombing raids. Shortages of components, particularly of the 12.8cm gun, further delayed production. Nibelungen-Werke completed 48 Jagdtigers during late 1944 and a further 25 vehicles during the first three months of 1945. The last four Jagdtigers completed were delivered to the 653rd Army Heavy Anti-tank Battalion during the first week of April 1945.

The few Jagdtigers that entered German service were allocated to a very small number of independent heavy anti-tank battalions. One such unit, the 512th Army Heavy Anti-tank Battalion, was formed in February 1945 from the remnants of the 424th (formerly 501st) Heavy Tank Battalion, which had been decimated in January 1945, resisting the Soviet offensive east of the River Vistula. In operational terms, the Jagdtiger was a very heavy and largely immobile vehicle, though such deficiencies were less significant in the defensive battles that Germany fought in the last year of the war. The Jagdtiger's best tactical use was as a static defensive pillbox, hull-down behind cover or situated in built-up areas, where its formidable 12.8cm gun could inflict considerable damage on attacking Allied armour.

Jagdtiger in Combat: Operation 'Northwind'

The few Jagdtigers deployed to the front in the last six months of World War II provided valuable reinforcement for the desperate defensive combat the German Army conducted, as it slowly retreated into the Reich. But on the rare occasions during the last year of the war when the German Army resumed the offensive, the Jagdtiger proved less effective. During the Battle of the Bulge, for example, the Germans deployed nine Jagdtigers to support the attack. These Jagdtigers belonged to the 653rd Army Heavy Anti-

ABOVE *American troops inspect a knocked-out Jagdtiger. The soldier at the rear has opened the double doors set in the superstructure rear that provide access to the fighting compartment. Several skirting plates have come off during combat – a common occurrence.*

tank Battalion which was part of the Fifth Panzer Army's strategic reserve. Having recognised that these lumbering tank destroyers were of little use in the restricted hilly terrain of the Ardennes, the Germans held them in reserve, intending to unleash them into the battle once German forces had reached more suitable terrain beyond the River Meuse. The early stalling of the counter-offensive, however, meant that the Jagdtigers were never deployed into the attack.

Instead, the 653rd Battalion redeployed south to the Saar area, where the Germans then attempted a surprise attack amid the snow falling on New Year's Eve. This new attack – designated Operation 'Northwind' (Nordwind) – represented an attempt by the Germans to salvage some success from the failure of the Ardennes counter-offensive. The Jagdtigers played a prominent role in 'Northwind' and at least one of the 653rd's nine Jagdtigers was destroyed by Allied fire near Rimling during the course of the offensive.

But after initial successes, the attacking German forces were steadily driven back with heavy casualties, as the Allies reacted and brought to bear their numerical superiority. The fate of 'Northwind' mirrored precisely what had just occurred in the Battle of the Bulge - German attempts to drive back the Allies on the Western Front in the last six months of the war were doomed to failure. After the demise of 'Northwind', the German Army concentrated all its remaining Jagdtigers in the 653rd Battalion. On 1 April 1945, this unit fielded 23 operational Jagdtigers, though all were apparently lost in the last month of the war during the final desperate German battle to slow the inexorable Allied conquest of the Nazi Reich.

LUCHS

The Panzerkampfwagen (2cm) II Luchs (Lynx) armoured car was a fully tracked armoured reconnaissance vehicle based on the standard Panzer II tank. During late 1942, after Panzer II production had ended, the German Army developed the VK1301, a prototype fast reconnaissance vehicle, based on this tank, which ultimately developed into the Luchs.

Light tanks such as this had their origins in the cavalry tanks of 20 years before, which, in turn, were a direct replacement for the horse cavalry itself. The role of the light tank was one of reconnaissance, scouting and pursuit, and for this it needed to be (as its name suggests) light and poorly armoured – its speed being its main form of protection.

Originally the German Army classified the vehicle as a tank – the Panzer II Model L – but soon redesignated the Luchs as a dedicated fully tracked reconnaissance vehicle. The Luchs was produced jointly by Daimler-Benz, which developed the superstructure and the turret, and MAN, which developed the chassis. The initial order was for 800 Luchs. In the end, just 131 Luchs armoured cars were produced between 1943 and January 1944.

The Luchs was a 12-tonne (11.8-ton) vehicle operated by a crew of four. It mounted the standard Panzer II tank turret, an important difference being that Luchs' turret did not have a cupola or vision ports. Instead it was designed with two revolving periscopes which were attached to the turret roof. In addition, the superstructure had been widened to extend over the tracks, thus allowing a larger turret to be mounted. The turret also carried the standard Panzer II 2cm KwK 38 gun and coaxial 7.92mm machine gun. The last 31 vehicles produced, however, mounted the much larger 5cm KwK 39 L/60 gun in this small turret. This was at best a clumsy mismatch of gun and turret.

The suspension of the Luchs had five sets of interleaved large bogie wheels and no return rollers. Powered by a 180bhp Maybach HL 66P petrol engine, the Luchs could achieve an impressive maximum road speed of 60kph (37mph) – a feature that was crucial to its role as a fast reconnaissance vehicle.

From 1943, the Luchs served exclusively in the armoured reconnaissance battalions of German panzer divisions on both the Eastern and Western Fronts until 1945. Though attrition steadily reduced their numbers, a few examples of this rare vehicle remained in active service until the end of the war.

SPECIFICATIONS: Panzerkampfwagen (2cm) II Luchs (Sdkfz 123)

GENERAL
Vehicle Type: fully tracked, armoured reconnaissance vehicle (light recce tank)
Entered Service: spring 1943
Crew: four
Combat Weight: 11.8 tonnes
(11.6 tons)

DIMENSIONS
Overall Length: 4.63m (15ft 2in)
Hull Length: 4.63m 15ft 2in)
Width: 2.49m (8ft 2in)
Height: 2.13m (7ft)

ARMAMENT
Main: 2cm (0.8in) KwK 30 L/55 gun
Secondary: 1 x 7.92mm (0.312in) MG 34 coaxial in turret

AMMUNITION STOWAGE
Main: 330 rounds
Secondary: 2250 rounds

ARMOUR
Hull Front (Nose): 30mm (1.2in)
(at 65 degrees)
Hull Front (Driver's Plate): 20mm
(0.8in) (at 90 degrees)
Hull Sides: 20-30mm (0.8–1.2in)
(at 85–90 degrees)
Hull Rear: 20mm (0.8in) (at 60 degrees)
Turret Front: 30mm (1.2in)
(at 80 degrees)
Turret Sides: 15mm (0.6in)
(at 70 degrees)
Turret Rear: 20mm (0.8in)
(at 70 degrees)

Turret Roof: 13mm (0.5in)
(at 0–10 degrees)

MOTIVE POWER
Engine: Maybach HL 66 P R6-cylinder petrol
Power: 180 bhp
Fuel capacity: 236 litres (52 gallons)

PERFORMANCE
Maximum Road Speed:
60kph (37mph)
Maximum Cross-Country Speed:
42kph (26mph)
Operational Range (Road): 150km
(93 miles)
Operational Range (Cross-Country):
95km (59 miles)

PANZER MAUS

The enormous Panzer Maus (Mouse) super-heavy tank was the culmination of Germany's increasing wartime fixation with ever larger tanks.

On 8 June 1942, Adolf Hitler gave a verbal contract to Professor Porsche to develop a prototype super-heavy tank, designated with intended irony as the Maus. In August 1943, Alkett commenced work on the first prototype, with Krupp producing the turret and main armament. By June 1944, Alkett had completed installation of the turret and gun onto its chassis and delivered the prototype to the German Army. Alkett duly completed a second prototype a few months later.

The German Army conducted extensive trials with these two vehicles from late 1944 at the Kummersdorf training grounds. The Maus, however, never saw active service and the Germans destroyed both vehicles in April 1945, before the Soviets occupied the area.

The Maus carried a massive 15cm KwK 44 L/38 gun as main armament as well as a co-axial 7.5cm KwK 44 L/36.5 gun. As each 15cm shell alone weighed 70kg (154 lb), the tank's ammunition had to be carried on a separate trailer to avoid overloading an already heavy vehicle. The Maus possessed an extremely high standard of protection, thanks to armour-plate that

was an incredible 240mm- (9.5in-) thick and 200mm- (7.9in-) thick on the front and sides, respectively. The Maus weighed a colossal 191 tonnes (188 tons), equivalent to the weight of 35 Panzer I tanks, or even of three Jagdtigers! The turret alone weighed 50 tons, more than a Panther tank. To power this massive beast, Daimler-Benz developed a new 1200bhp MB 509 V12-cylinder petrol engine, but it was so fuel-hungry that the second prototype received a 1200bhp MB 517 water-cooled diesel engine instead. Both vehicles could manage a maximum road speed of just 20kph (12.5mph).

This monstrosity was little more than a barely mobile pill box and was useless as a tank. No bridge could support the vehicle's weight and its cross-country mobility was very limited. Within the menagerie of weird German vehicles, the Panzer Maus was the most worthless dissipation of scarce resources.

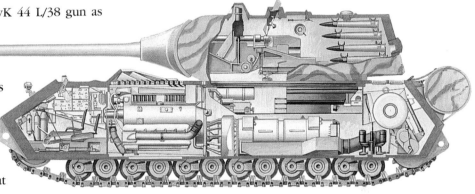

SPECIFICATIONS: Panzer Maus (No Sdkfz No.)

GENERAL
Vehicle Type: super-heavy tank
Entered Service: n/a (two prototypes completed late 1944)
Crew: six
Combat Weight: 188 tonnes (185 tons)

DIMENSIONS
Overall Length: 10.08m (33ft 1in)
Hull Length: 9.03m (29ft 7in)
Width: 3.67m (12ft)
Height: 3.66m (12ft)

ARMAMENT
Main: 15cm (5.9in) KwK 44 L/38; plus coaxial 7.5cm (3in) KwK 44 L/36.5
Secondary: 2 x 7.92mm (0.312in) MG 34; I coaxial in turret; I fitting on roof for anti-aircraft MG

AMMUNITION STOWAGE
Main: 50 rounds (carried in separate trailer)
Secondary: 1000 rounds

ARMOUR
Hull Front (Nose): 200mm (7.9in) (at 60 degrees)
Hull Front (Driver's Plate): 200mm (7.9in) (at 35 degrees)
Hull Sides: 180mm (7.1in) (at 90 degrees)
Hull Rear: 160–165mm (6.3–6.5in) (at 90 degrees)
Turret Front: 240mm (9.5in) (n/k)
Turret Sides: 200mm (7.9in) (at 60 degrees)
Turret Rear: 200mm (7.9in) (at 60 degrees)

Turret Roof: 60mm (2.4in) (at 0 degrees)

MOTIVE POWER
Engine: Daimler Benz MB 509 V12-cylinder petrol (Maus #2 = MB 517 V12-cylinder diesel)
Power: 1200 bhp
Fuel capacity: 4800 litres (1056 gallons)

PERFORMANCE
Maximum Road Speed: 20kph (12.5mph)
Maximum Cross-Country Speed: 11kph (7mph)
Operational Range (Road): 190km (119 miles)
Operational Range (Cross-Country): 97km (60 miles)

STURMPANZER IV BRUMMBÄR

The Sturmpanzer IV Brummbär (Grizzly Bear), also known as the Sturmpanzer 43 (Sdkfz 166), was an armoured heavy assault howitzer based on the chassis of the Panzer IV tank. The vehicle was designed to engage heavily fortified bunkers and to participate in urban street combat. The Brummbär carried as its main armament a ball-mounted very short-barrelled (12-calibre) 15cm StuH 43 assault howitzer. German firms mounted this weapon in a heavily protected, enclosed superstructure or fighting compartment that was fitted on top of the standard chassis of the Panzer IV Model E–G tanks.

Alkett developed the Brummbär, and also designed the superstructure itself, while Krupp designed the chassis. The superstructure was box-like and heavily protected by frontal armour which measured some 100mm-

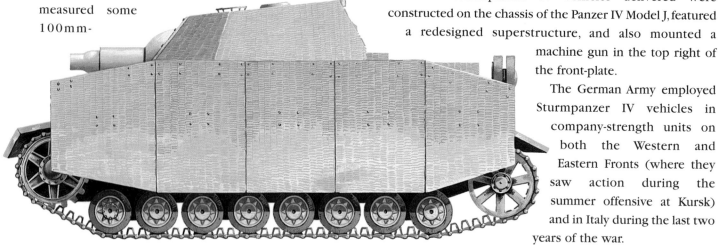

(4in-) thick, plus 50mm (2in) plate on the sides and 40mm- (1.6in-) thick armour on the rear. Thanks to the large gun and heavy armour that the vehicle carried, the Sturmpanzer IV weighed a substantial 31.1 tonnes (30.6 tons). The Brummbär was powered by a 300bhp Maybach HL 120 TRM V12-cylinder petrol engine, which enabled the vehicle to achieve, when moving by road, a maximum speed of 40kph (25mph) and an effective operational range of 210km (131 miles).

German factories completed a total of 306 Sturmpanzer 43 vehicles, in three slightly different versions, during a production run that lasted between April 1943 and March 1945. Early vehicles featured a driver's visor, whereas mid-production Brummbärs had this replaced by a periscope. The last Sturmpanzer IV vehicles delivered were constructed on the chassis of the Panzer IV Model J, featured a redesigned superstructure, and also mounted a machine gun in the top right of the front-plate.

The German Army employed Sturmpanzer IV vehicles in company-strength units on both the Western and Eastern Fronts (where they saw action during the summer offensive at Kursk) and in Italy during the last two years of the war.

SPECIFICATIONS: Sturmpanzer IV (Sturmpanzer 43) Brummbär (Sdkfz 166)

GENERAL
Vehicle Type: infantry assault vehicle (self-propelled assault howitzer)
Entered Service: spring 1943
Crew: five
Combat Weight: 28.3 tonnes (27.8 tons)

DIMENSIONS
Overall Length: 5.89m (19ft 4in)
Hull Length: 5.89m (19ft 4in)
Width: 3.73m (12ft 3in)
Height: 3.46m (11ft 4in)

ARMAMENT
Main: 15cm (5.9in) StuH 43 L/12
Secondary: 1 x 7.92mm (0.312in) MG 34 in hull front.

AMMUNITION STOWAGE
Main: 36 rounds
Secondary: 600 rounds

ARMOUR
Hull Front (Nose): 50+50mm (2+2in) (at 75 degrees)
Hull Front (Driver's Plate): 80mm (3.2in) (at 78 degrees)
Hull Sides: 20+20mm (0.8+0.8in) (at 90 degrees)
Hull Rear: 20mm (0.8in) (at 80–82 degrees)
Superstructure Front: 100mm (4in) (at 50 degrees)
Superstructure Sides: 20–60mm (0.8–2.4in) (at 65-88 degrees)
Superstructure Rear: 30mm (1.2in) (at 64–90 degrees)

Superstructure Roof: 20mm (0.8in) (at 6 degrees)

MOTIVE POWER
Engine: Maybach HL 120 TRM V12-cylinder petrol
Power: 300 bhp
Fuel capacity: 470 litres (103 gallons)

PERFORMANCE
Maximum Road Speed: 40kph (25mph)
Maximum Cross-Country Speed: 24kph (15mph)
Operational Range (Road): 210km (131 miles)
Operational Range (Cross-Country): 130km (81 miles)

STURMPANZER VI STURMTIGER

The extremely rare Sturmpanzer VI Sturmtiger was a heavy assault tank variant of the Tiger I. The vehicle mounted a short-barrelled 38cm RW61 L/5.4 mortar projector designed to blast both heavy concrete fortifications and large buildings. This weapon could fire a massive 376kg (761lb) shell up to a range of 5500m (18,044ft). Given that these rounds were so heavy, the vehicle could only carry 13 projectiles and had to mount a small crane to help the five-man crew handle the rounds. The Sturmtiger also possessed heavy armour protection. Both the vehicle's main armament and heavy armour protection contributed to it weighing a colossal 68 tonnes (66.9 tons). A 700bhp Maybach V12-cylinder petrol engine powered the Sturmtiger and enabled the vehicle to obtain, when travelling by road, both a maximum speed of 40kph (25mph) and an effective operational range of 120km (75 miles).

In August 1944 the firm of Alkett converted into Sturmtiger assault vehicles some 18 damaged Tiger I tanks that had been returned to its factory for repairs. The German Army allocated these 18 Sturmtigers to three assault mortar companies – each with a theoretical establishment of 14 vehicles – intended for use in urban street warfare or in operations against heavily fortified enemy defences. In late 1944, the German Army employed these units both on the Eastern Front and in Italy.

In December 1944, the 1000th and 1001st Assault Mortar Companies – together fielding just seven Sturmtigers – were

earmarked for participation in the German Ardennes counter-offensive. The Sixth Panzer Army, the spearhead German formation in the Ardennes, held these vehicles in reserve to provide heavy fire support should any urban combat occur. These ponderous vehicles, however, were thoroughly unsuited to the tactical requirements of the counter-offensive, which demanded a rapid advance through the narrow, winding and hilly roads of the Ardennes. In fact, the lumbering Sturmtigers advanced far to the rear of the more agile Panzer IV and Panther tanks and even then still struggled to keep pace with them, and so in reality made a very modest contribution to the German counter-offensive.

SPECIFICATIONS: Sturmpanzer VI Sturmtiger (No Sdkfz No.)

GENERAL
Vehicle Type: heavy assault vehicle (self-propelled assault mortar)
Entered Service: summer 1944
Crew: five
Combat Weight: 68 tonnes (66.9 tons)

DIMENSIONS
Overall Length: 6.31m (20ft 8in)
Hull Length: 6.31m (20ft 8in)
Width: 3.73m (12ft 3in)
Height: 3.46m (11ft 4in) (including crane)

ARMAMENT
Main: 38cm (15in) Mörser RW61 L/5.4 mortar projector
Main Gun Traverse: 10 degrees left to 10 degrees right

Secondary: 1 x 7.92mm (0.312in) MG 34 in hull front

AMMUNITION STOWAGE
Main: 13 rounds
Secondary: 800 rounds

ARMOUR
Hull Front (Nose): 150mm (5.9in) (at 66 degrees)
Hull Front (Driver's Plate): 150mm (5.9in) (at 80 degrees)
Hull Sides: 80mm (3.2in) (at 90 degrees)
Hull Rear: 80mm (3.2in) (at 82 degrees)
Superstructure Front: 150mm (5.9in) (at 45 degrees)
Superstructure Sides: 80mm (3.2in) (at 70 degrees)

Superstructure Rear: 80mm (3.2in) (at 80 degrees)
Superstructure Roof: 40mm (1.6in) (at 0 degrees)

MOTIVE POWER
Engine: Maybach HL 230 P45 V12-cylinder petrol
Power: 700 bhp
Fuel Capacity: 540 litres (119 gallons)

PERFORMANCE
Maximum Road Speed: 40kph (25mph)
Maximum Cross-Country Speed: 24kph (15 mph)
Operational Range (Road): 120km (75 miles)
Operational Range (Cross-Country): 85km (37 miles)

NASHORN

Geschützwagen III/IV chassis had its engine moved well forward, a reconfiguration that produced a larger compartment at the rear of the vehicle.

The German Army Weapons Department issued contracts for the construction of the Nashorn in February 1942 and the first vehicles entered service with independent army heavy anti-tank battalions during November 1942. Deutsche Eisenwerke completed 473 Nashorn tank destroyers during a production run that continued into 1944.

The Nashorn mounted the powerful 8.8cm Pak 43/1 L/71 anti-tank gun. The Germans desperately wished to mount this potent weapon in an effective armoured fighting vehicle, because the towed Pak 43/1 anti-tank gun was too large for troops to manoeuvre easily. The Geschützwagen III/IV chassis, however, could scarcely carry the weight of the Pak 43/1 gun, and so the armour possessed by the Nashorn had to be very light. The Nashorn was yet another stopgap that certainly packed a lethal punch but lacked adequate protection. During 1944, the Nashorn was increasingly replaced in army heavy anti-tank battalions by a more effective tank destroyer, the Jagdpanzer V Jagdpanther.

The Nashorn (Rhinoceros) was another improvised German self-propelled anti-tank gun or primitive tank destroyer developed in haste in the middle years of the war, to counter the Soviet tank menace. The Nashorn, originally named the Hornisse (Hornet) until Hitler personally changed it, was an unusual tank destroyer because it was based on an uncommon hybrid chassis, designated the Geschützwagen (Gun Carriage) III/IV. In early 1942, the armaments firms of Alkett and Deutsche Eisenwerke developed this tracked platform using parts from both the standard Panzer III and IV tank chassis. The

---

SPECIFICATIONS: Nashorn (Sdkfz 164)

GENERAL
Vehicle Type: tank destroyer (self-propelled anti-tank gun)
Entered Service: early 1942
Crew: five
Combat Weight: 24 tonnes (23.6 tons)
Chassis: Gun Carriage III/IV (hybrid Panzer III/IV)

DIMENSIONS
Overall Length: 8.44m (27ft 8in)
Hull Length: 5.80m (19ft 2in)
Width: 2.95m (9ft 8in)
Height: 2.65m (8ft 8in)

Armament
Main: 8.8cm (3.5in) PaK 43/1 L/71
Main Gun Traverse: 15 degrees left to

15 degrees right
Secondary: none

AMMUNITION STOWAGE
Main: 40 rounds
Secondary: none

ARMOUR
Hull Front (Nose): 30mm (1.2in) (at 78 degrees)
Hull Front: (Driver's Plate): 30mm (1.2in) (at 35 degrees)
Hull Sides: 20mm (0.8in) (at 90 degrees)
Hull Rear: 20mm (0.8in) (at 80 degrees)
Superstructure Front: 10mm (0.4in) (at 60 degrees)
Superstructure Sides: 10mm (0.4in) (at 74 degrees)

Superstructure Rear: 10mm (0.4in) (at 80 degrees)
Superstructure Roof: none

MOTIVE POWER
Engine: Maybach HL 120 TRM V12-cylinder petrol
Power: 300 bhp
Fuel Capacity: 470 litres (103 gallons)

PERFORMANCE
Maximum Road Speed: 40kph (25mph)
Maximum Cross-Country Speed: 24kph (15 mph)
Operational Range (Road): 200km (124 miles)
Operational Range (Cross-Country): 130km (81 miles)

PANZERJÄGER TIGER (P) ELEFANT

The Elefant (Elephant) was an improvised heavy tank destroyer produced in mid-1943 from 90 discontinued Porsche VK4501 (P) prototype Tiger tank chassis. The Panzerjäger Tiger (P) Elefant (Sdkfz 184), originally named the Ferdinand, was a very heavily armoured but rather immobile tank destroyer that mounted a potent gun. The Elefant was designed in haste as another stop-gap vehicle that utilised both existing chassis and guns to augment German anti-tank capability against the Soviets.

Rather unusually, the Elefant was powered not by one, but by two 320bhp Maybach HL 120 TR engines. However, the sheer bulk of the vehicle and its extremely high ground pressure figure – 20 percent greater than that of the ponderous King Tiger – severely restricted its mobility. The Elefant also experienced extensive mechanical problems

that were exacerbated by shortages in replacement parts. The Elefant's over-emphasis on firepower and protection exerted a heavy toll on both its mobility and mechanical reliability: all told, the vehicle was an unbalanced design that proved an operational disappointment.

The German High Command hurriedly dispatched the 90 Elefants completed in mid-1943 to the Eastern Front, so that they could participate in the German Kursk offensive of July 1943. At Kursk, the Germans employed these vehicles in two independent, heavy motorised anti-tank battalions. Within the first four days of the offensive, however, several dozen Elefants had broken down due to chronic mechanical problems. The vehicle's lack of a machine gun for close-quarter defence proved a critical weakness, with another 20 or so Elefants falling victim to short-range Soviet anti-tank weapons.

In early 1944, the German Army redeployed the few Elefants that had survived the debacle at Kursk to Italy. By early 1945, all these vehicles had succumbed either to Allied fire or irreparable mechanical failure during the slow fighting withdrawal that the Germans had conducted up the Italian peninsula.

SPECIFICATIONS: Panzerjäger Tiger (P) Elefant (Sdkfz 184)

GENERAL
Vehicle Type: heavy tank destroyer (heavy self-propelled anti-tank gun)
Entered Service: summer 1943
Crew: six
Combat Weight: 68 tonnes (66.9 tons)
Chassis: Porsche VK4501(P) Tiger prototype

DIMENSIONS
Overall Length: 8.14m (26ft 8in)
Hull Length: 6.80m (22ft 4in)
Width: 3.43m (11ft 3in)
Height: 2.97m (9ft 9in)

ARMAMENT
Main: 8.8cm (3.5in) PaK 43/2 L/71 gun
Main Gun Traverse: 14 degrees left to 14 degrees right

Secondary: none

AMMUNITION STOWAGE
Main: 50 rounds
Secondary: none

ARMOUR
Hull Front (Nose): 100+100mm (3.9+3.9in) (at 75 degrees)
Hull Front (Driver's Plate): 200mm (7.9in) (at 90 degrees)
Hull Sides: 80mm (3.2in) (at 90 degrees)
Hull Rear: 80mm (3.2in) (at 90 degrees)
Superstructure Front: 200mm (7.9in) (at 60 degrees)
Superstructure Sides: 80mm (3.2in) (at 60 degrees)
Superstructure Rear: 80mm (3.2in) (at 60 degrees)

Superstructure Roof: 40mm (1.6in) (at 5 degrees)

MOTIVE POWER
Engine: 2 x Maybach HL 120 TR V12-cylinder petrol
Power: 2 x 320 = 640 bhp
Fuel Capacity: 950 litres (210 gallons)

PERFORMANCE
Maximum Road Speed: 20kph (12.5mph)
Maximum Cross-Country Speed: 15kph (9.5mph)
Operational Range (Road): 150km (93 miles)
Operational Range (Cross-Country): 90km (56 miles)

WESPE

The Wespe (Wasp) became the best-known German self-propelled artillery vehicle of World War II. The Wespe mounted the standard 10.5cm (4.1in) light field howitzer in a thinly armoured fighting compartment on top of a modified Panzer II chassis. The vehicle was officially designated the 10.5cm Le.F.H. 18/2 auf Fahrgestell Panzer II (sf) Wespe (Sdkfz 124), or 10.5cm Light Field Howitzer 18/2 mounted on the self-propelled Panzer II chassis Wasp. During 1942, Alkett, MAN and Rheinmetall-Borsig collaborated to finalise the Wespe design, while subsequent production was carried out by Famo of Warsaw.

The Wespe mounted the 10.5cm (4.13in) howitzer in an open-topped, box-like superstructure that sloped downwards towards the rear. Mounting this large gun on a small chassis, however, restricted the ammunition stowage to just 40 rounds. Equipped with a muzzle brake, the 10.5cm howitzer produced a muzzle velocity of 470 metres per second (1542 feet per second) when firing standard high-explosive shells. Protection for the vehicle consisted of 10mm- (0.4in-) thick plate on the superstructure and a maximum of 18mm-(0.7in-) thick armour on the hull.

Between 1942 and late 1944, Famo completed 683 Wespe vehicles either from newly fabricated chassis or by converting obsolete Panzer II tanks. The Wespe saw service in German panzer and panzer grenadier divisions. Theoretically, every battery also contained a Wespe munitions carrier that could hold an additional 90 rounds of ammunition. German firms constructed 158 of these carriers by removing either the main armament from the standard Wespe vehicle, or the turret from aged Panzer II tanks.

SPECIFICATIONS: Wespe (Sdkfz 124)

GENERAL
Vehicle Type: self-propelled artillery gun
Entered Service: summer 1942
Crew: five
Combat Weight: 11.5 tonnes (11.3 tons)
Chassis: Panzer II

DIMENSIONS
Overall Length: 4.79m (15ft 8in)
Hull Length: 4.79m (15ft 8in)
Width: 2.24m (7ft 4in)
Height: 2.32m (7ft 7in)

ARMAMENT
Main: 10.5cm (4.1in) leFH 18/2 L/28 howitzer
Main Gun Traverse: 17 degrees left to 17 degrees right

Secondary: none

AMMUNITION STOWAGE
Main: 32 rounds
Secondary: none

ARMOUR
Hull Front (Nose): 20mm (0.8in) (at 75 degrees)
Hull Front (Driver's Plate): 20mm (0.8in) (at 60–75 degrees)
Hull Sides: 15mm (0.6in) (at 90 degrees)
Hull Rear: 20mm (0.8in) (at 90 degrees)
Superstructure Front: 12mm (0.5in) (at 69 degrees)
Superstructure Sides: 10mm (0.4in) (at 73 degrees)

Superstructure Rear: 10mm (0.4in) (at 74 degrees) or none
Superstructure Roof: none

MOTIVE POWER
Engine: Maybach HL 62 TR R6-cylinder petrol
Power: 140 bhp
Fuel Capacity: 170 litres (37 gallons)

PERFORMANCE
Maximum Road Speed: 40kph (25mph)
Maximum Cross-Country Speed: 20kph (12.5 mph)
Operational Range (Road): 140km (87 miles)
Operational Range (Cross-Country): 95km (59 miles)

HUMMEL

The Hummel (also nicknamed the Bumble-Bee) was a heavy self-propelled artillery vehicle which mounted the 15cm (5.9in) heavy field howitzer in a lightly armoured superstructure, which was fitted on top of the hybrid Geschützwagen III/IV chassis. The vehicle, which had been designed by Alkett during 1942, was officially designated the 15cm Armoured Howitzer 18/1 on the Gun Carriage III/IV (Sdkfz 165).

On 27 February 1944, Hitler ordered that the vehicle's name be dropped because he thought it too timid for a fighting vehicle. The Geschützwagen III/IV chassis incorporated design features of both the Panzer III and IV tanks. In fact, the chassis was essentially a front-engined Panzer IV that utilised the sprockets and final drive of the Panzer III tank. A few late-production Hummel vehicles, however, were constructed on the conventional Panzer IV chassis due to a shortage of hybrid chassis.

The Hummel weighed a substantial 25.9 tonnes (25.5 tons), largely due to the size of its howitzer. To prevent overloading of the chassis, the vehicle's design saved weight by restricting the stowage of 15cm ammunition to just 18 rounds. In addition, weight was also saved by providing the Hummel with only light protection.

The firm of Deutsche Eisenwerke constructed 666 Hummels at an average rate of 35 units per month during a production run that lasted between December 1942 and June 1944. Six Hummel vehicles equipped the solitary heavy self-propelled battery within each armoured artillery battalion that the panzer divisions possessed. Deutsche Eisenwerke also constructed 150 gun-less Hummel munitions carriers, one of which was assigned to each Hummel battery.

SPECIFICATIONS: Hummel (Sdkfz 165)

GENERAL
Vehicle Type: self-propelled heavy artillery gun
Entered Service: spring 1943
Crew: six
Combat Weight: 23.5 tonnes (23.1 tons)
Chassis: Gun Carriage III/IV (hybrid Panzer III/IV)

DIMENSIONS
Overall Length: 7.17m (23ft 6in)
Hull Length: 5.80m (19ft 2in)
Width: 2.92m (9ft 7in)
Height: 2.81m (9ft 3in)

ARMAMENT
Main: 15cm (5.9in) sFH 18/1 L/30 howitzer

Main Gun Traverse: 12 degrees left to 12 degrees right
Secondary: 1 x 7.92mm (0.312in) MG 34 in hull front

AMMUNITION STOWAGE
Main: 15 rounds
Secondary: 600 rounds

ARMOUR
Hull Front (Nose): 30mm (1.2in) (at 55 degrees)
Hull Front (Driver's Plate): 30mm (1.2in) (at 74 degrees)
Hull Sides: 10mm (0.4in) (at 90 degrees)
Hull Rear: 10mm (0.4in) (at 79 degrees)
Superstructure Front: 30mm (1.2in) (at 57 degrees)

Superstructure Sides: 10mm (0.4in) (at 76 degrees)
Superstructure Rear: 10mm (0.4in) (at 79 degrees)
Superstructure Roof: none

MOTIVE POWER
Engine: Maybach HL 120 TRM
Power: 300 bhp
Fuel Capacity: 470 litres (103 gallons)

PERFORMANCE
Maximum Road Speed: 42kph (26mph)
Maximum Cross-Country Speed: 24kph (15 mph)
Operational Range (Road): 215km (134 miles)
Operational Range (Cross-Country): 130km (81 miles)

BIBLIOGRAPHY

Anon., *Hitler's Panzers* (London, Marshall Cavendish, 1974)

Chamberlain, Peter and Ellis, Chris, *PzKpfW VI Tiger and Tiger II (Profile AFV 48)* (Windsor, Berks, Profile Publications, 1972)

Chamberlain, P. and Doyle, H.L., *The Panzerkampfwagen III and IV Series* (Bromley, Iso-Galago, 1989)

Duncan, Major-General N.W., *Panzerkampfwagen I and II (Profile AFV 15)* (Windsor, Profile Publications, 1970)

Edwards, Roger, *Panzer: A Revolution in Warfare 1939-1945* (London, Arms and Armour Press, 1989)

Ellis, Chris and Doyle, Hilary, *Panzerkampfwagen* (Kings Langley, Herts, Bellona, 1976)

Feist, Uwe and Nowarra, H. J., *The German Panzers from Mark I to the Mark V Panther* (Fallbrook, Calif., Aero Publishers, 1966)

Feist, Uwe, *Deutsche Panzer 1917-1945* (Fallbrook, Calif., Aero Publishers, 1978)

Fey, Willi, *Panzer in brennpunckt der Fronten* (Munich, 1960)

Fürbringer, Herbert, *9SS-Panzer Division Hohenstauffen 1944: Normandie-Tarnopol-Arnhem* (Paris, Editions Heimdal, 1984)

Gander, Terry, *Small Arms, Artillery and Special Weapons of the Third Reich* (London, Macdonald & Jane's, 1978)

Grove, Eric, *German Armour 1939-1940: Poland and France* (New Malden, Almark, 1976)

Grove Eric, *World War II Tanks: The Axis Powers: Germany, Italy, and Japan* (London, Orbis Publishing, 1978)

Guderian, Heinz, *Panzer Leader* (London, Futura, 1974)

Harris, J. P. and Toase, F. H. eds., *Armoured Warfare* (London, St. Martin's Press, 1990)

Jentz, Tom, et al., *King Tiger (Osprey New Vanguard 1)*, (London, Osprey, 1993)

Kurowski, Franz, *Die Panzer Lehr Division* (Bad Nauheim, Podzun, 1964)

Kurowski, Franz and Tornau, Gottfried, *Sturmartillerie Fels in der Brandung* (Herford, Maximilian, 1965)

Kurowski, Franz and Tornau, Gottfried, *Sturmartillerie 1939-45* (Stuttgart, Motorbuch, 1977)

Lefevre, Eric, *Battle of the Bulge: Then and Now* (London: Battle of Britain Ltd, 1984)

Lefevre, Eric, *Panzers in Normandy: Then and Now* (London: Battleline Books, 1984)

Luther, Craig W. H., *Blood and Honour: the History of 12th SS Panzer Division 'Hitler Youth' 1943-1945* (San Jose, Calif., Bender, 1987)

Macksey, Kenneth, *Tank Warfare: A History of Tanks in Battle* (London, Rupert-Hart Davis, 1971)

McLean, Donald B., *Illustrated Arsenal of the Third Reich* (Wickenburg, Ar., Normount Technical Publications, 1973)

Meyer, Hubert, *Kriegsgeschichte der 12SS-Panzerdivision "Hitlerjugend"* (Osnabrück, Munin Verlag, 1982)

Mellenthin, F. W. von, *Panzer Battles: A Study of the Employment of Armour in the Second World War* (Norman, Ok., Oklahoma University Press, 1968)

Müller-Hillebrand, Buckhardt, *German Tank Maintenance in WWII* (Washington, D.C., United States Government Printing Office, 1982)

Nehring, Walther, *Die Geschichte der Deutschen Panzerwaffe 1916 bis 1945* (Berlin, Propylaen, 1969)

Nowarra, Heinz J., *German Tanks 1914-1968* (New York, Arco, 1968)

Ogorkiewicz, Richard M., *Armour: The Development of Mechanised Forces and their Equipment* (London, Atlantic Books, 1960)

Perret, Bryan, *Panzerkampfwagen I. (Osprey Vanguard 18)* (London, Osprey, 1980)

Perret, Bryan, *German Light Panzers 1932-42 (Osprey Vanguard 33)* (London, Osprey, 1983)

Ross, G. MacCleod, *The Business of Tanks* (Ilfracombe, Arthur H. Stockwell, 1976)

Rütgen, Helmut, *Die Geschichte der Panzer Lehr Division im Westen* (Stuttgart, Motorbuch, 1979)

Reynolds, Michael, *Steel Inferno: I SS Panzer Corps in Normandy* (New York: Sarpedon, 1997)

Senger und Etterlin, Ferdinand M., *German Tanks of WWII: The Complete Illustrated History of German Armoured Fighting Vehicles* (Harrisburg, Stackpole Books, 1969)

Spielberger, Walter, *Panzerkampfwagen III (Profile AFV 2)* (Windsor, Profile Publications, 1970)

Spielberger, Walter, *Panzerkampfwagen IV (Profile AFV 43)* (Windsor, Profile Publications, 1972)

Spielberger, Walter J., *Beute-Kraftfahrzeuge und Panzer der deutschen Wehrmacht* (Stuttgart, Motorbuch, 1989)

Weeks, John, *Men Against Tanks: The History of Anti-tank Warfare* (New York, Mason/Charter, 1975)

White, B.T., *German Tanks and Armoured Fighting Vehicles, 1914-1945* (Shepperton, Ian Allen, 1966)

INDEX